Treasury of Classroom Arithmetic Activities

Treasury of

Classroom

Arithmetic

Activities

Joseph Crescimbeni

Professor of Education
Jacksonville University

Parker Publishing Company, Inc.
West Nyack, N.Y.

TREASURY OF CLASSROOM
ARITHMETIC ACTIVITIES

by Joseph Crescimbeni

©1969, BY

PARKER PUBLISHING COMPANY, INC.
West Nyack, N. Y.

LIBRARY OF CONGRESS
CATALOG CARD NUMBER: 69-11981

PRINTED IN THE UNITED STATES OF AMERICA
B & P

The Author's Other Books:

Arithmetic Enrichment Activities for Elementary School Children

Teaching the New Mathematics

Guiding the Gifted Child

Individualizing Instruction in the Elementary School

An Overview of American Education

Guide for Student Teachers

The author extends his thanks to the many students in his University classes who contributed ideas, suggestions, and topics to this book. Special gratitude must be given to Gail Mayer and Barbara Thomas who did many of the illustrations.

This book is dedicated to

M _____

A Word From the Author

Children in elementary schools are curious and eager to apply their minds and experiences to the challenge of classroom activities. They are anxious to try new ideas, solve problems, and tackle different learning games. Because the teaching process must be one of *personal interaction,* between the teacher and the learner and the learner and the learning experience, instructional aids that are creative and challenging must be applied to the school curriculum.

This is the role of enrichment activities, and in mathematics education, children can be motivated by learning aids that are fascinating and challenging in structure. Mathematical games, puzzles, brain teasers, and other learning devices play a definitive role in the process of learning. Children like them, teachers appreciate them, and parents notice a mathematical sensitivity to arithmetic instruction in the children who use them.

The purpose of this book is to list some of the newer and more proven classroom arithmetic enrichment aids, which teachers will find applicable to the basic mathematical concepts found in the elementary mathematics curriculum. Used as supplemental experiences to the regular mathematics program, these enrichment aids help stimulate interest in the teacher's daily lesson plan in arithmetic instruction. They re-inforce mathematical motivation when learning has a tendency to decline. They spur initiative in children who achieve success in mathematical competencies and who wish to further their capabilities in this area. They also serve a basic purpose of individualizing mathematical instruction to children who need special assistance in identified computational deficiencies.

Sensory and visual aids not only improve understanding but allow children to attain a curiosity and satisfaction toward the completion of mathematical tasks. The enrichment activities presented in this book are basic to this purpose. If the teacher uses them with discretion and direction in her daily program, learning can truly become an objective of *personal worth* for every child, and mathematics instruction will become a treasury of practical concepts and experiences.

Joseph Crescimbeni

Table of Contents

1

Anagrams and
Cryptograms

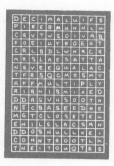

Anagrams

Here is one way to play anagrams. The game is to add one letter to a word to make a new word. The letters may be moved about, for example:

ONE + S = NOSE

The answers to the ten anagrams below are arithmetic words. Find these words:

1. DAY + R =	6. WEARS + N =
2. RAP + I =	7. SHAVE + L =
3. TIN + P =	8. TINNY + E =
4. STIR + F =	9. CLINK + E =
5. CONES + D =	10. RESUME + A =

Answers

1. YARD	6. ANSWER
2. PAIR	7. HALVES
3. PINT	8. NINETY
4. FIRST	9. NICKEL
5. SECOND	10. MEASURE

Hidden Words

Ten arithmetic words are written below. The letters in each word have been replaced by figures. Each figure stands for the same letter in all the numbers. Can you find the ten hidden words?

1.	240	6.	6037
2.	199	7.	27544
3.	0604	8.	27659
4.	8165	9.	06042440
5.	8602	10.	27652440

Answers

1.	ten	6.	inch
2.	add	7.	three
3.	nine	8.	third
4.	pair	9.	nineteen
5.	pint	10.	thirteen

Scrabble

Arrange the following letters into mathematical terms:

1. nitoqeau   _____

2. lqeau   _____

3. dddnea   _____

4. denrtbusah   _____

5. endumin   _____

6. endvidid   _____

7. ductpro   _____

8. wasner   _____

Answers: 1. equation
               2. equal
               3. addend
               4. subtrahend
               5. minuend
               6. dividend
               7. product
               8. answer

Addition Brain Teaser

Exchange one number in the first column for a number in the second column so that both columns add up to the same number:

0	6
2	1
7	5
9	8

Answer: switch the 0 and the 1. sum is 19.

A Word Maze

Eleven arithmetic words are hidden in the square below. Can you find them? Here are the rules. You may start in any square and move in any direction to any square next to it. You may continue to move one space in any direction until a word is made. But you must not enter the same square twice while spelling a word. To get you started, the word INCH has been marked in the square. Now find the other ten hidden words.

Y	T	W	H
A	T	E	C
R	I	N	O
N	D	P	U

Answers

Count, inch, nine, ninety, one, ounce, pint, pound, ten, twenty, yard.

Can you find 11 arithmetic words in this square?

S	X	T	Y
I	U	R	E
F	O	M	E
H	D	Z	N

Answers

Dozen, forty, four, fourteen, hour, more, six, sixteen, sixty, sum, zero.

Word Blocks

Hidden in the block below are three different arithmetic words. Each word has three different letters. The word is made by taking one letter from each line across. Can you find it?

The answer to the word block above is ONE, SIX, TWO.

Do you know the rules? Remember, for each word only one letter must be taken from any line across. Now find three arithmetic words in each of the following blocks.

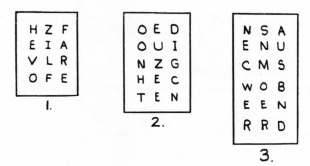

Answers

1. half, zero, five
2. ounce, eight, dozen
3. number, second, answer

Letter Puzzles

A Cute Car

You can move the letters of "A Cute Car" around to make a word that you use in arithmetic. The word means "correct," or "free from mistakes." The word begins with ac.

$$\text{1} \quad \text{2 3 4 5} \quad \text{6 7 8}$$
$$\text{A} \quad \text{CUTE} \quad \text{CAR}$$

The next letter after ac is the sixth letter in the words above. Write the sixth letter, then the third letter, then the eighth, the seventh, the fourth, and the fifth. What word did you get?

Answer: ACCURATE

Slip It Mule

Move the letters around and make a word that you often use in arithmetic. The word begins with m.

1 2 3 4	5 6	7 8 9 10
S L I P	I T	M U L E

The second letter of the "hidden" word is the eighth letter in the three words above. Now you have mu. Can you finish writing the word?

Answer: MULTIPLIES

If Nor Cat

These three words do not make sense. By moving the letters around, you can make a word that is important in arithmetic. What is the word?

Answer: FRACTION

Jumbled Words

The words below are good arithmetic words. The trouble is that the letters have been moved around a little. Can you put the letters back in their right order?

DAD	EON	ROME	LOTTA	CAB-STRUT
NET	CHIN	ZONED	GRUFIE	FEE-TO-RUN

Answers

ADD	ONE	MORE	TOTAL	SUBTRACT
TEN	INCH	DOZEN	FIGURE	FOURTEEN

Eye Tester

Find these mathematical terms in this puzzle. They may be found in any direction—vertical, horizontal, diagonal, backward, and forward. Letters may be used more than once.

D	E	C	I	M	A	L	U	I	F	S
P	I	R	E	B	M	U	N	N	L	U
C	R	V	T	W	S	O	I	V	A	B
F	O	E	I	U	Y	R	O	E	H	T
C	R	L	B	D	L	W	N	R	C	R
M	R	S	L	A	E	S	A	T	T	A
N	E	V	E	E	Q	U	A	L	A	C
T	F	R	S	Q	C	M	O	S	M	T
A	F	F	M	U	L	T	I	P	L	Y
R	I	R	N	I	B	M	I	X	E	D
D	D	A	G	V	H	S	O	O	T	N
N	E	C	B	A	S	E	E	D	N	E
M	G	T	C	L	O	S	E	T	E	U
E	N	I	L	E	L	A	C	S	M	N
D	D	O	S	N	U	L	L	X	E	I
C	O	N	N	T	R	O	O	T	L	M
T	N	E	I	T	O	U	Q	T	E	S

Mean	Even
Real	Odd
Sign	Collection
Mixed	Equal
Root	Scale
Close	Number
Law	Decimal
Mode	Differ
Open	Multiply
Line	Equivalent
Match	Union
Subset (2)	Theory
Quotient	Subtract
Divide	Element
Half	Set
Minuend	Base
Term	Null
Sum	Fraction
Invert	Add

Scrambles

You'll always find
this in the yard.

NTE

UORF

FEIV

OZRE

Puzzle Word

See the letters NTE, UORF, FEIV, OZRE. Each set of letters can be moved around to make an arithmetic word. Make a copy of the squares. Then write each letter in a square to spell a word. The letters NTE make the word TEN. The letters UORF make the word FOUR. The letters FEIV make the word FIVE. The letters OZRE make the word ZERO.

Use the letters TOFO that fall in the darkened squares to make the puzzle word. The puzzle word is also an arithmetic word. Now solve the two "scrambles" that follow.

Light, but not as
light as a feather.

Puzzle Word   TAQUR

UDONP

NICH

Answers   MIDE
(quart, pound,
inch, dime)
OUNCE

All this work for
nothing!

Puzzle Word

VENSE

NEZOD

TROFY

RETHE

Answers
(seven, dozen,
forty, three)
ZERO

Cryptograms

Look at the key code listed below for each of the letters of the
alphabet.

a = 1	i = 9	q = 17	
b = 2	j = 10	r = 18	
c = 3	k = 11	s = 19	
d = 4	l = 12	t = 20	y = 25
e = 5	m = 13	u = 21	z = 26
f = 6	n = 14	v = 22	
g = 7	o = 15	w = 23	
h = 8	p = 16	x = 24	

Now match each of the following exercises with the letters after
you have done the operation. Then find the sentence that is spelled
out.

Add

```
    6 0 1  9    5 1 11   1    0 10 1 2  7    2 21 0
+   4 1 2  2    3 0  8   0    2  2 01  4    3  4 5
   10 1 3 11    8 1 19   1    2 12 1 3 11    5 25 5

    J  a c  k    h a  s   a    b  l  a c  k    e  y e.
```

Now do these examples on your own:

Multiply

2 3 3 4	4 3 1 5 19	1 1	19 5 2 1 3 4	11 5 6 5	23 5 6 3
x 1 3 4 3	4 4 1 5 1	2 1	1 1 1 1 4 3	2 1 3 5	1 1 2 4

Answer: Bill plays baseball very well.

Subtract

20 5 20 11	15 9 22	20 10 6	8 12 8 9 15 9 24
− 10 4 6 6	7 8 3	0 2 1	1 3 1 2 3 4 5

Answer: Jane has the giggles.

Decipher a Message—Code Base 5

2 - 22 - 11—101 - 14 - 42—101—14 - 42 - 101 - 30

32 - 101 - 24 - 42 - 13—100 - 22 - 23 - 43.

Step I:

Change the base 5 numbers to base 10 numbers.

2 - 12 - 6—26 - 9 - 22—26—9 - 22 - 26 - 15

17 - 26 - 14 - 22 - 8—25 - 12 - 13 - 23.

Step II:

Using the Alphabet Code, change the numbers
to letters to spell out the message:

A = 26	F = 21	K = 16	P = 11	U = 6	Z = 1
B = 25	G = 20	L = 15	Q = 10	V = 5	
C = 24	H = 19	M = 14	R = 9	W = 4	
D = 23	I = 18	N = 13	S = 8	X = 3	
E = 22	J = 17	O = 12	T = 7	Y = 2	

2 - 12 - 6—26 - 9 - 22—26—9 - 22 - 26 - 15

Y - O - U   A - R - E   A   R - E - A - L

17 - 26 - 14 - 22 - 8—25 - 12 - 13 - 23.

J - A - M - E - S   B - O - N - D.

Write Your Name in "Code Base 8"

Alphabet is in base 10 numbers.

A = 26	F = 21	K = 16	P = 11	U = 6	Z = 1
B = 25	G = 20	L = 15	Q = 10	V = 5	
C = 24	H = 19	M = 14	R = 9	W = 4	
D = 23	I = 18	N = 13	S = 8	X = 3	
E = 22	J = 17	O = 12	T = 7	Y = 2	

Write your name in letters, then change the letters to base 10 numbers:

M   A   R   Y
14, 26, 9, 2

Change these base 10 numbers to base 8 numbers:

16, 32, 11, 3

Secret code message!

A=1	G=7	M=13	S=19	Y=25
B=2	H=8	N=14	T=20	Z=26
C=3	I=9	O=15	U=21	
D=4	J=10	P=16	V=22	
E=5	K=11	Q=17	W=23	
F=6	L=12	R=18	X=24	

The total sum of each problem is one code number. The total of these 15 problems spells out a secret code!

42	6	7	10	12	26	27
-41	×3	+2	×2	-4	-13	-22

4	3	3	20	11	2	7	20
×5	×3	×1	-11	+ 8	×3	×3	-6

<u>Answer</u>: ARITHMETIC
IS FUN.

Mystery Message

Find the answer to this message by solving the equations, locating the answer in the lettered section, and placing the letter-answers in the appropriate blanks.

$$\underline{\ }\ \underline{\ }\ \underline{\ }\ \underline{\ }\ \underline{\ }\ \underline{\ }\ \underline{\ }\ \underline{\ }\ \underline{\ }\ \underline{\ }\ \underline{\ }\ \underline{\ }\ \underline{\ }\ \underline{\ }\ \underline{\ }\ \underline{\ }\ !$$
a b c d e f g h i j k l m n o p

a. $2 \times 3 = \square$	A - 3	N - 5
b. $4 - 1 = \square$	B - 9	O - 20
c. $8 + 3 = \square$	C - 14	P - 16
d. $7 + \square = 8$	D - 4	Q - 25
e. $\square + 6 = 9$	E - 1	R - 13
f. $5 + \square = 10$	F - 15	S - 22
g. $4 \times 3 = \square$	G - 18	T - 7
h. $\square - 7 = 7$	H - 6	U - 26
i. $2 + 4 - 5 = \square$	I - 12	V - 11
j. $1 \times 2 \times 4 = \square$	J - 21	W - 8
k. $(0 + 4) - 3 = \square$	K - 10	X - 24
l. $\square + 0 = 1$	L - 23	Y - 2
m. $4 + 2 + 4 = \square$	M - 17	Z - 19
n. $2 + 3 - 4 = \square$		
o. $9 - \square = 4$		
p. $2 \times 1 \times 2 = \square$		

Answer

HAVE A NICE WEEKEND!

2

Brain Twisters

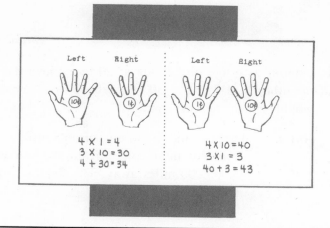

Left   Right   Left   Right

4 X 1 = 4
3 X 10 = 30
4 + 30 = 34

4 X 10 = 40
3 X 1 = 3
40 + 3 = 43

Some Brain Teasers

The Paper Test

Most books are about 6 x 9 inches, and each page is of normal thickness. Suppose you had a sheet of paper and cut it in half, then you cut the half in half, and kept cutting into halves 30 times. Then you put all of the sheets you cut on top of one another in one big pile. How large would the sheet of paper have to be that you began with in order to have the *final cutting* 6 x 9 inches? How high do you think the pile would be after 30 cuttings?

> *Answer:* The original piece of paper would have to be 16 square miles in area, and after 30 cuttings the pile would be 25 miles high.

The Boat Test

A boat is anchored in a harbor, and a rope ladder hangs down to the water from the railing of the boat to the edge of the water. There is a distance of 1 foot between each rung of the ladder, and there are ten rungs showing.
If the tide comes in at 1½ feet per hour, how many rungs would be showing at the end of 5 hours?

> *Answer:* Ten rungs. The boat would rise with the incoming tide.

The Shadow Test

An albatross is a large flying bird. It has a wingspan of about 12 feet. If two of these birds were flying over an empty parking lot at noon, with one bird flying at 20 feet above the ground and the other bird flying at 300 feet above the ground, which bird would cast the longest shadow?

Answer: There would be no measurable difference. The source of light comes from the sun which is 93,000,000 miles away. The shadows would be the same.

Telling Your Age

Ask a friend to multiply his age by 2. $2 \times 9 = 18$

Then have him add 5 to the product. $18 + 5 = 23$

Multiply that sum by 5. $5 \times 23 = 115$

Add the number of people there are in your
family. (Suppose there are 4.) $115 + 4 = 119$

When finished, subtract 25 from your number. $119 - 25 = 94$

The answer you get will tell your age and the
number of people in your family.   Age is 9

4 is number in family

Another Age Trick

This trick can only work with someone who is between 11 and 19 years of age. Let us pick number 13.

1. Multiply your age by 4. $4 \times 13 = 52$

2. Add your age to this product. $52 + 13 = 65$

3. Multiply the result by 2. $65 \times 2 = 130$

4. Subtract 99. $130 - 99 = 31$

5. Tell me the sum of the figures in your answer. $3 + 1 = 4$

The person is 13 years old. The only teen number having figures that add to 4 is the number 13. (1 + 3 = 4, 13.)

Counting to a Million

How long do you think it would take to count up to *one million* if we used one number every second?

Give an estimate first and then work the problem out. Was your solution close to your estimate?

Procedure: You can count to 60 in one minute, using one second for every number. You can then multiply by 60 minutes and get 3,600 numbers for one hour.

If we divide 1,000,000 by 3,600, we get 277. The number 277 (rounded off) represents the number of hours.

We then divide the number of hours by 24 hours in one day:

$$277 \div 24 = 11\frac{1}{2} \text{ days}$$

Counting day and night, it would take you about 11½ days to count from number 1 to 1,000,000 using one number per second.

Spending a Million Dollars

If someone gave you a million dollars and you were asked to spend *one dollar a minute,* how long do you think it would take? Estimate first, and then work out your answer:

Procedure: One dollar per minute for an hour would be 60 dollars per hour. Multiply 60 dollars per hour by 24 hours and you get $1,440 dollars per day.

Divide $1,000,000 by $1,440 and it comes out to 694.4 days.

Spending a million dollars at a dollar per minute would then take you about 694½ days or about 23 months.

St. Ives Question

Read the following jingle. Can you determine the total number?

While I was going to the village of St. Ives,
I met a man with 7 wives.
And each wife had 7 cats
And each cat had 7 kits.
Kits, cats, man, and wives
Guess how many are going to St. Ives?

Answer: **400**   1 man
7 wives
49 cats
343 kits
400

A Number Riddle

I'm one more ten than forty.
5 tens in all you see.

My starting letter is an F   *Answer:* 50
The end one sounds like E.

Add one to myself
The sum is ninety-four.
That should be sufficient   *Answer:* 93
I shall say no more.

Problem in Arrangement

Arrange these cards in pairs so that all pairs have the same total:

2   4   6   8   10   12
14   16   18   20   22   24

Answer: All pairs total 26. The pairs are:

2-24   4-22   6-20   8-18   10-16   12-14

Rapid Service Calculations

Ask a friend to select any number from the table below. He must then tell you in which columns the selected numbers appear. You can tell him what his number is with accuracy in rapid time.

Suppose he selects the number 20 and tells you it appears in columns C and E. In column C you find 4 and add it to the 16 which appears in Column E. Add the top number in each column only.

Suppose he selects number 15 and tells you the number appears in columns A, B, C, and D. Then all you do is add the first four numbers in these columns: 1 + 2 + 4 + 8. This is equal to 15.

Practice this trick with yourself a few times.

A	B	C	D	E
1	2	4	8	16
11	18	5	13	24
9	11	14	11	18
5	14	13	24	22
13	7	7	10	17
17	10	22	i4	19
3	22	6	15	20
19	3	28	26	23
15	6	20	27	26
23	19	15	28	27
27	15	23	31	28
31	23	31	12	30
21	26	30	30	31
25	27	29	29	29
29	31	25	9	21
7	30	12	25	25

The 3945 Trick (for the year 1969)

Write the number 3945 on a piece of paper, fold it, and then hide it.

1. Tell a friend to write down the year he was born.

He writes   1960

2. Now write the number of days in a week. He writes   7

3. Now the year he entered school. Suppose he writes   1966

4. Now write his age.   He writes   9

5. Write the number of years he has attended school.

He writes   3

6. Tell him to add up all the numbers.   3945

Then show him your hidden number: 3945

How it works: All of the numbers equal 3945, which is the same as 2 x 1969 + 7.

The year your friend was born in plus his age equals 1969. The number of days in a week is always 7. There is your answer.

In 1970 the number is 3947, in 1971 it is 3949, in 1972 it is 3951, etc.

I Know Your Number

Read this problem over a few times to make sure you understand it. Then you can challenge your friends with it.

What You Do	*What Your Friend Does*
1. Write any number that is less than 99. For example, write 64. Fold the paper and hide it in your pocket or in your friend's pocket.	
2. Tell your friend to write down any number between 50 and 100.	Suppose he writes 72.
3. Now, mentally subtract the number you wrote (64), from 99, and you get 35. Tell your friend to add 35 to the number he wrote down.	He gets 107.

4. Now tell your friend to cross out the first digit and add it to the remaining digits.

He crosses out the 1 and adds it to 07 making 08.

5. Now tell your friend to subtract this number from the original number he wrote down. Take away 08 from 72.

He writes 64.

6. At this point, you show him the paper that you wrote your number on. . .and there is 64 — the same number as his.

To do this trick with higher numbers, the number you select must be between 100 and 200, while the number your friend selects can be any one between 200 and 1,000. In the third step, instead of taking your original number from 99, subtract it from 999.

Just Fun

Write the answers to the following questions in a column:

1. In what year were you born?
2. In what year did something important happen to you?
3. How many years from then until now?
4. What is your age on your birthday this year?

Add your answers and divide by 2. The answer will be the present year. Can you figure out why this works?

Answer: If you add the first and last numbers together you will get the present year. If you add the two middle numbers together you will get the present year. They are adding 2 times the present year by following directions, and then dividing the sum by 2.

Guess Their Ages

Joe is four times as old as Ray, but in 30 years Ray will be only half as old as Joe. How old are they now?

Answer: The ratio of Joe's age to Ray's will change in 30 years. from 4 to 1 to 2 to 1. Since the period of 30 years equals the difference of the two ratios, then,

30 x 2 = 60, Joe's age

and

½ x 30 = 15, Ray's age.

Toothpick Teasers

Here are four problems worked with toothpicks. You see, of course, that each statement is not true. Can you move just one toothpick to change each statement to a true statement?

$$III - II = IV$$

$$I - III = II$$

$$VI - IV = IX$$

$$VI - X = IV$$

Answers

III + I = IV

I = III − II

VI + IV = X

VI = X − IV

How Much for Candy

Earl's mother gave him some money to buy some candy. On the way out the door, his father gave him another 8 cents to spend. His candy cost exactly 20 cents. He had only 20 cents. How much did his mother give him?

Answer: 12 cents   (20 − 8)

The Clock Problem

Martha wound her clock four times and set it for 7:00 a.m. Her sister, Joyce, set her electric clock for 8:00 a.m. During the night, the electricity went off for two hours. In the morning, both girls woke up at 6:00 a.m. In order for both clocks to read the correct hour, how many hours should each girl move her clock forwards or backwards?

Answer: Joyce can look at Martha's windup clock for the correct time because it was not affected by the electricity power loss.

The Brick Problem

If a brick balances evenly with three-fourths of a pound and three-quarters of a brick, what is the weight of a whole brick?

Answer: A whole brick weighs 3 pounds.

The Socks Problem

If in your bureau drawer there are ten blue socks and 16 grey socks, and you reach into it in the dark, how many socks must you take out to be sure of getting a pair that match?

Answer: 3 socks

Frog in the Well

A frog is at the bottom of a 32 foot well. Each day he jumps up 5 feet but during the night he slides down 2 feet. How many days will it take him to jump out of the well? Remember, the frog must jump 5 feet each day.

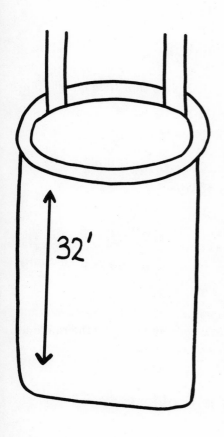

32'

1st day—up 5 feet and slides down 2 = 3

2nd day—up 5 feet and slides down 2 = 3

3rd day—up 5 feet and slides down 2 = 3

4th day—up 5 feet and slides down 2 = 3

5th day—up 5 feet and slides down 2 = 3

6th day—up 5 feet and slides down 2 = 3

7th day—up 5 feet and slides down 2 = 3

8th day—up 5 feet and slides down 2 = 3

9th day—up 5 feet and slides down 2 = 3

At this point he has progressed 27 feet

10th day—up 5 feet and out of the well because he has now jumped 32 feet.

The Number 45

Divide the number 45 into four parts so that adding 2 to the first part, subtracting 2 from the second part, multiplying the third part by 2, and dividing the fourth part by 2 will all give the same answer:

Solution: break 45 down to: 8   12   5   20

$$8 + 2 = 10$$
$$12 - 2 = 10$$
$$5 \times 2 = 10$$
$$20 \div 2 = 10$$

The 100 Problem

Write the digits: 9, 8, 7, 6, 5, 4, 3, 2, 1 so that they equal 100, writing them in the order that was given.

Answer: $98 - 76 + 54 + 3 + 21 = 100$

Making a Chain

I have six sections of a chain, each consisting of four links. If the cost of cutting open a link is 10 cents, and welding it together again is 25 cents, how much will it cost to have the six pieces joined into one chain?

Solution: $1.40   First cut open all four links of one section and use these four links to join the remaining five sections together.

The Toy Horse Problem

Larry has 20 toy horses in a box. He has 12 black horses and eight white horses. He asks his friend, Tom, to pick out two horses of the same color without looking.

How many horses must Tom choose to get two horses of the same color?

> *Answer:* Three. Here are the possibilities:
>
> > 2 white and 1 black horse
> > 2 black and 1 white horse
> > 3 white horses
> > 3 black horses

How Many Are There?

1. How many 5's are there in 555? _____
2. How many 3's are there in 3,333? _____
3. How many 2's are there in 442? _____
4. How many 4's are there in 20,128? _____
5. How many 1's are there in 211? _____

Answer: There are two possible solutions for each example:

> 1. 3 or 111
> 2. 4 or 1,111
> 3. 1 or 221
> 4. 0 or 5,032
> 5. 2 or 211

The Fly Problem

There are two flies in a quart jar. They double themselves every 24 hours, and at the end of ten days the jar is full. There are 2,048 flies in the jar. When (what day) was the jar half-full?

> *Answer:* On the 9th day.

1st day: 2 x 2 = 4

2nd day: 4 x 2 = 8

3rd day: 8 x 2 = 16

4th day: 16 x 2 = 32

5th day: 32 x 2 = 64

6th day: 64 x 2 = 128

7th day: 128 x 2 = 256

8th day: 256 x 2 = 512

9th day: 512 x 2 = 1,024   (half-full)

10th day: 1,024 x 2 = 2,048

A Troublesome Fraction

If I doubled ⅕ of a fraction and multiplied it by that fraction, I would get ¹⁄₁₀. What do you think my original fraction was?

Answer: The original fraction is ½ *or* ⁵⁄₁₀. One fifth of ⁵⁄₁₀ times 2 is ²⁄₁₀ and multiplied by ½ is equal to ¹⁄₁₀.

Dividing 64

Try to divide the number 64 into two parts, so that if each part is divided by 4 the two quotients when added together will be ¼ of the original number.

Answer: The two parts of 64 must be 40 and 24. If you divide 40 and 24 by 4, the quotients will be 10 and 6. The sum of 10 and 6 or 16 is ¼ of 64.

The Dinner Problem

Ellen decides to have a little party and she is going to invite four of her classmates: Mary, Margaret, Nancy, and Donna. How many ways can she seat these people next to her at the table?

Answer: 24 different ways.
Ellen will be first
then
1 x 2 x 3 x 4 = 24 positions.

Water in the Jar

A man is down by the stream. He is told to bring back 4 quarts of water; no more and no less. He has 2 jars: a 5 quart jar and a 3 quart jar. There are no measurements on these jars. All he knows is that one jar holds 5 quarts and the other one 3 quarts. How is he going to bring back 4 quarts?

Answer

The man fills up the 3 quart jar with water and pours it into the 5 quart jar. Then he fills up the 3 quart jar with water for a second time and pours it into the 5 quart jar, as much as it will hold. Thus, he is only able to put 2 more quarts into the 5 quart jar and has 1 quart left over in the 3 quart jar. Now he pours all of the water out of the 5 quart jar. He takes the 1 quart left over in the 3 quart jar and pours it into the 5 quart jar. Then he fills up the 3 quart jar again. Now he takes the filled 3 quart jar and pours this into the 5 quart jar making 4 quarts.

Where Is the Penny?

1. Ask a friend to hold a dime and a penny for you. Have him put the dime in one hand and the penny in the other.
2. Have him multiply the value of the coin in his right hand by 4, 6, or 8.
3. Have him multiply the value of the coin in his left hand by 3, 5, or 7.
4. Now have him add the two results and tell you their sum.

Answer

If the sum is even (ends in 4, 6, or 8), the penny is in his right hand.

If the sum is odd (ends in 3, 5, or 7), the penny is in his left hand.

| Left | Right | | Left | Right |

$$4 \times 1 = 4$$
$$3 \times 10 = 30$$
$$4 + 30 = 34$$

$$4 \times 10 = 40$$
$$3 \times 1 = 3$$
$$40 + 3 = 43$$

Multiplication—The Long Way

There is a way of multiplying that does not multiply large numbers or use fractions. All you do is multiply and divide by 2, and no other number. Yet, you always get the exact answer to a problem.

Here is how it works: Let us multiply 54 x 67

$$54 \text{ x} \quad\quad 67$$
$$27 \text{ x} \quad\quad 134$$
$$13 \text{ x} \quad\quad 268$$
$$6 \text{ x} \quad\quad 536$$
$$3 \text{ x} \quad 1,072$$
$$1 \text{ x} \quad 2,144$$

You divide the numbers in the first column by 2, and multiply those in the second column by 2. When you see that half of 27 is 13½ and half of 13 is 6½, drop the fractions.

Cross out all the *even* numbers in the first column going over to column 2. Then, add all the remaining numbers in column 2.

$$
\begin{array}{rr}
\cancel{54}\text{x} & \cancel{67} \\
27\text{ x} & 134 \\
13\text{ x} & 268 \\
\cancel{6}\text{x} & \cancel{536} \\
3\text{ x} & 1{,}072 \\
1\text{ x} & \underline{2{,}144} \\
& 3{,}618
\end{array}
$$

Check: 54 x 67 = 3,618.

Try this number: 15 x 47

$$
\begin{array}{rr}
15\text{ x} & 47 \\
7\text{ x} & 94 \\
3\text{ x} & 188 \\
1\text{ x} & \underline{376} \\
& 705
\end{array}
$$
(add the numbers in the right column)

Check: 15 x 47 = 705

Easy with Eleven

This is an easy trick for multiplying any double digit number by 11 such as: 17 x 11. To do this problem quickly look at the following steps:

add 1 + 7 = 8

place the 8 between the 7 and the 1

you now have 187 which is the answer.

Check: 17
             x 11
             ____
               17
             17
             ____
             187

Now try with a tougher number like: 89 x 11.

Add 8 + 9 = 17.

Put the 7 between the 8 and 9 (carry the one).

Change the 8 to the 9 so the answer will be:

                    979

       Check: 89
                    x 11
                    ____
                      89
                    89
                    ____
                    979

Look at these: 33 x 11 = 363

                    42 x 11 = 462

                    55 x 11 =

                    76 x 11 =

                    92 x 11 =

Adding in Two Seconds

You can add up large numbers in about two seconds. You can amaze your friends this way, but you must practice first.

Ask a friend to write down a number from each of the five columns in this table. As soon as he does, you add the *five last digits* mentally, then subtract this number from 50 and tack it on to the result.

A	B	C	D	E
69	345	186	872	756
366	642	582	278	558
168	246	87	575	657
762	147	285	377	954
663	543	483	179	855
564	48	384	674	459

Let us say your friend selects: 168 543 285 674 and 756.

You add up: $8 + 3 + 5 + 4 + 6$. You get 26.

Subtract 26 from 50 and you get 24.

Tack the 24 to the 26 and you get *2,426* which is the answer.

(Always put the number you subtract from 50 *before* the five digits you add.)

Writing Problem Equations

Read the following problem and write a correct equation to solve the problem. Then solve the problem:

There are 35 children in our room. Fifteen are boys.
Half the girls have blue eyes. How many girls do *not* have blue eyes?

$$\frac{35 - 15}{2} = \frac{20}{2} = 10$$

Answer: 10 girls do not have blue eyes.

Now work out this problem:

Some children in a sixth grade went to the auditorium. Two-thirds of the children are still sitting in the class. The principal sent for some more children to go to his office, which left only

½ of the children sitting in the class. What part of the class did the principal send for the second time?

> *Answer:* $\frac{2}{3} - n = \frac{1}{2}$
>
> or   ⅙ of the class left
> the second time.

Roman Numerals

Which Roman numerals can be read either upside down or right side up at *all* times?

> *Answer:*   I   II   III   XXX   X   XIX   XX

Trick Riddles

Trick riddles continually amaze people. Sometimes, it is *how the trick is said.* Other times, it is just a case of *not understanding* what is said. Either way, look at these riddles and see if your children respond to them accurately the first time. If not, explain to them why they did not interpret the riddle correctly.

R.   What is the difference between a new penny and a dime?

> *Answer:*   Nine cents

R.   Susan says, "I can drop a fresh egg 3 feet without breaking it." How can Susan win her bet?

> *Answer:*   She dropped it 4 feet. It fell 3 feet without breaking.

R.   If you take three apples from five apples, how many do you have?

> *Answer:*   Three. You have the three you took.

R.   There are twelve 1 cent stamps in a dozen. Then how many 2 cent stamps are there in a dozen?

Answer: Twelve. A dozen is a dozen.

R. What becomes larger when turned upside down?

Answer: 6. It becomes 9.

R. What is the difference between twice forty-five and twice five and forty?

Answer: Forty. $2 \times 45 = 90$
$2 \times 5 = 10$
$10 + 40 = 50$
$90 - 50 = 40$

R. What is the difference between a man hammering a nail and a grocer selling a pound of coffee?

Answer: One pounds away, while the other weighs a pound.

R. Elizabeth stands with both feet on a scale and weighs 60 pounds. How much does she weigh when she lifts one foot?

Answer: The same, 60 pounds.

R. How many marbles can you place in an empty plastic quart container?

Answer: One. After that, the container is no longer empty.

R. If it takes three minutes to boil one egg, how many minutes does it take to boil three eggs?

Answer: Three minutes. Boil all the eggs at one time.

R. An empty barrel weighs ten pounds. What can you put in the barrel to make it weigh eight pounds?

Answer: Holes. Making holes removes some of the wood and makes the barrel lighter.

R. Which is correct to say: "Six and seven *is* fourteen?" or "Six and seven *are* fourteen?"

Answer: Neither, 6 + 7 = 13.

R.   What goes up and never comes down?

   Answer: Your age.

R.   Can you figure out when eleven plus four equals three?

   Answer: Eleven o'clock plus four hours equals three o'clock.

R.   A man had 20 *sick* sheep and six of them died. How many did he have left?

   Answer: 20 − 6 = 14. He had 14 sheep left

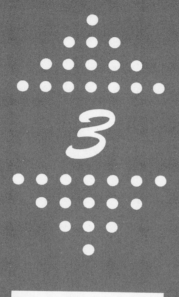

3

Crossnumbers

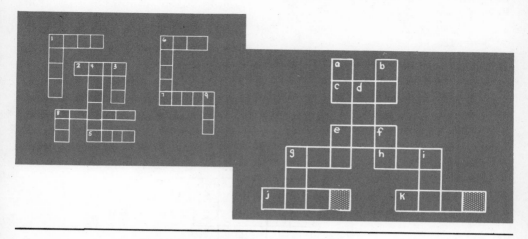

Crossword Number Puzzle

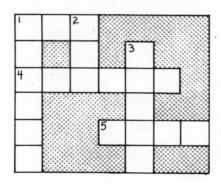

Across	*Down*
1. $4 - 2 =$	1. $10 + 10 =$
4. $2 + 6 + 1 + 2 =$	2. $7 - 6 =$
5. $6 - 6 =$	3. $2 + 3 + 2 =$

Answers

Across	*Down*
1. two	*1. twenty*
4. eleven	*2. one*
5. zero	*3. seven*

Crossnumber Puzzle

Skill-fixing practice sets in computation and problem solving increase interest when presented as crossnumber puzzles. Solve in the same manner as crossword puzzles. They may be varied in content and difficulty and may be constructed by upper-grade children.

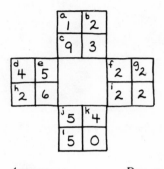

	Across		Down
(a) 3⟌36	(a) 79 − 60	(j) 11 × 5	
(c) 54 + 39	(b) 3⟌69	(K) 2⟌80	
(d) 5 × 9	(d) 61 − 19		
(f) 9⟌198	(e) 7 × 8		
(h) 13 × 2	(f) 13 + 9		
(i) 5⟌110	(g) 679 − 657		
(j) 6 × 9			
(l) 100 ÷ 2			

Adding

Across

(a)	36	(c)	6
	+ 25		7
			+ 5

(e)	68	(g)	38
	80		27
	+ 73		+ 79

(h)	8	(i)	40
	14		+ 52
	+ 55		

(j)	65
	78
	+ 62

Down

(a)	25	(b)	35
	+ 37		+ 92

(c)	39	(d)	45
	40		17
	+ 63		+ 22

(f)	82	(g)	96
	70		72
	+ 20		+ 27

Answer

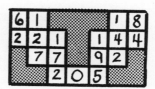

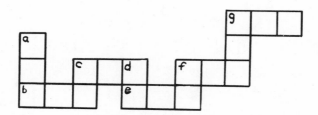

Across

(b)	53	(c)	88
	+ 58		+ 74

(e)	36	(f)	6
	17		89
	+ 63		+ 25

(g)	30
	20
	+ 50

Down

(a)	66	(c)	4
	+ 35		5
			+ 2

(d)	5	(f)	4
	7		7
	+ 9		+ 5

(g)	38
	45
	+ 47

Answer

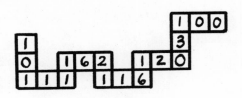

Subtracting

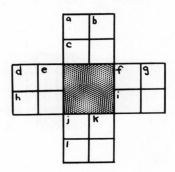

	Across				*Down*		
(a)	83	(c)	129	(a)	100	(b)	121
	– 54		– 85		– 76		– 27
(d)	144	(f)	130	(d)	164	(e)	95
	– 57		– 33		– 79		– 17
(h)	154	(i)	147	(f)	120	(g)	142
	– 96		– 63		– 22		– 68
(j)	105	(l)	110	(j)	129	(k)	154
	– 59		– 34		– 82		– 88

Answer

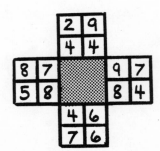

Writing Numbers

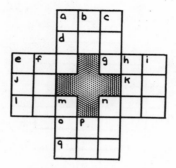

Across	Down
(a) Two hundred thirty-seven	(a) Two hundred nineteen
(d) One hundred eighty	(b) Thirty-eight
(e) Six hundred ninety-nine	(c) Seven hundred seven
(g) Seven hundred eleven	(e) Six hundred eighty-six
(j) Eighty-two	(f) Nine hundred twenty
(k) Forty-nine	(h) One hundred forty-seven
(l) Six hundred two	(i) One hundred ninety-five
(n) Four hundred seventy-five	(m) Two hundred fifty-seven
(o) Five hundred fifty	(n) Four hundred
(q) Seven hundred ten	(p) Fifty-one

Answer

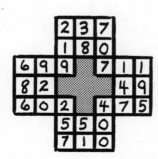

Multiplying

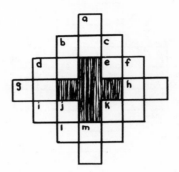

Across

(b) 43
  x 3

(d) 38
  x 2

(e) 17
  x 3

(g) 13
  x 4

(h) 25
  x 3

(i) 12
  x 7

(k) 20
  x 4

(l) 53
  x 8

Down

(a) 26
  x 2

(b) 16
  x 1

(c) 19
  x 5

(d) 91
  x 8

(f) 34
  x 5

(j) 22
  x 2

(k) 14
  x 6

(m) 5
  x 5

Answer

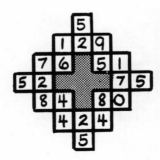

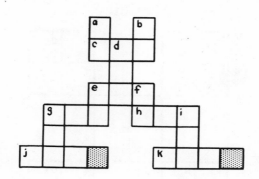

Across

(c)   54
   x 8

(e)   45
   x 9

(g)   44
   x 7

(h)   88
   x 3

(i)   22
   x 5

(k)   37
   x 3

Down

(a)   32
   x 2

(b)   24
   x 3

(d)   75
   x 4

(e)   16
   x 3

(f)   13
   x 4

(g)   39
   x 9

(i)   63
   x 7

Answer

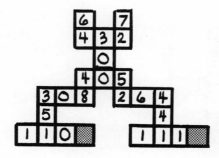

Dividing

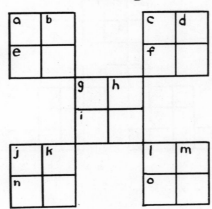

Across

(a) $6\overline{)186}$ (c) $3\overline{)189}$

(e) $4\overline{)128}$ (f) $9\overline{)180}$

(g) $5\overline{)305}$ (i) $8\overline{)168}$

(j) $3\overline{)126}$ (l) $2\overline{)68}$

(n) $7\overline{)287}$ (o) $6\overline{)60}$

Down

(a) $3\overline{)99}$ (b) $4\overline{)48}$

(c) $2\overline{)124}$ (d) $8\overline{)240}$

(g) $4\overline{)248}$ (h) $7\overline{)77}$

(j) $2\overline{)88}$ (k) $5\overline{)105}$

(l) $9\overline{)279}$ (m) $5\overline{)200}$

Answer

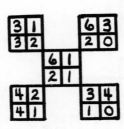

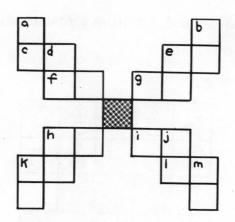

Across

(c) $6\overline{)246}$ (e) $4\overline{)168}$

(f) $8\overline{)80}$ (g) $3\overline{)216}$

(h) $5\overline{)250}$ (i) $6\overline{)426}$

(k) $9\overline{)189}$ (l) $4\overline{)128}$

Down

(a) $2\overline{)108}$ (b) $3\overline{)96}$

(d) $7\overline{)77}$ (e) $2\overline{)84}$

(h) $4\overline{)204}$ (j) $2\overline{)26}$

(k) $7\overline{)140}$ (m) $8\overline{)160}$

Answer:

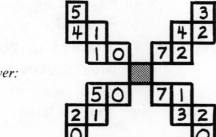

Multiplication and Addition Crossnumbers Puzzle

Purpose: To give pupils additional drill in multiplying and then adding a number to the product.

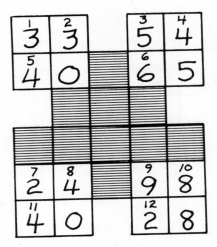

ACROSS

1. FIVE 6's, PLUS 3
3. SEVEN TIMES SEVEN PLUS FIVE
5. SEVEN FIVES PLUS 5
6. 10 SIXES PLUS 5
7. SEVEN THREES PLUS THREE
9. NINE TENS PLUS 8 ONES
11. 4 TIMES 9 PLUS 4
12. 9 X 3 PLUS 1

DOWN

1. PRODUCT OF 3 AND 9, PLUS 7
2. FOUR SEVENS PLUS TWO
3. NINE 6's PLUS TWO
4. PRODUCT OF 7 AND 6, PLUS 3
7. INCHES IN TWO FEET
8. FIVE SEVENS PLUS FIVE
9. TWO MORE THAN 9 X 10
10. 9 X 9 + 7

Crisscross Puzzle

Solve the number sentence and write the word in the puzzle.

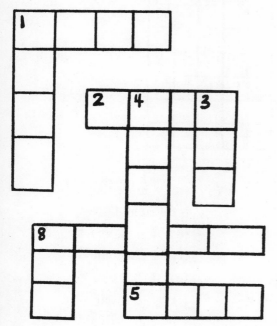

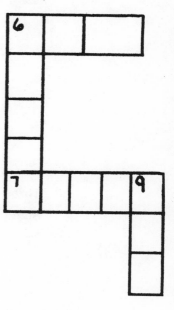

Across

(1) ☐ + 3 = 7

(2) 6 + △ = 6

(5) ◯ − 5 = 4

(6) 8 − 6 = ☆

(7) 4 + 4 = ☐

(8) ☆ + 2 = 9

Down

(1) 8 − 3 = ☐

(3) 6 − ◯ = 5

(4) 1 + ☆ = 12

(6) △ + 7 = 10

(8) 9 − ☐ = 3

(9) 5 + 5 = ◯

Reviewing

	a	b		c		
d		e	f			g
h	i				j	
	k			l		
m			n		o	p
		q		r		
	s			t		

Across

(a) Three 8's

(c) Sum of 12 and 18

(e) Multiply 48 by 4

(h) 28 + 33 =

(j) What is left when you take 87 from 100

(k) Four 9's

(l) Difference between 122 and 57

(m) Sum of 18, 16, and 15

(o) Five nickels

(q) Add: 76 and 47

(s) 2 less than 100

(t) Double 32

Down

(b) 8 more than 33

(c) Eight 4's

(d) 4, 4, 4, and 4

(f) 1 less than 100

(g) 3 times 21

(i) 1 less than 140

(j) 2 more than 150

(m) Four tens

(n) One dozen

(p) A half dollar

(q) Nine pairs

(r) Three dozen

Answer

	2	4		3	0	
1		1	9	2		6
6	1		9		1	3
	3	6		6	5	
4	9		1		2	5
0		1	2	3		0
	9	8		6	4	

Adding, Subtracting, Multiplying, and Dividing

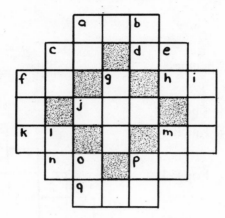

Across

(a) 26
  x 8

(c)   7
   38
  +21

(d) 100
  −82

(f) 110
  −85

(h) 6) 366

(j) 23
  x 8

(k) 42
   19
  +34

(m) 120
  −70

(n) 3) 129

(p) 105
  −30

(q) 50 + 82 + 70

Down

(a) 86
  −60

(b) 5) 405

(c) 104
  −39

(e) 134
  −48

(f) 69
   44
  +96

(g) 32
  x 9

(i) 25
  x 4

(l)   7
   34
  +13

(m) 18
   27
  +10

(o) 16
  x 2

(p) 4) 288

Answer

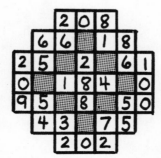

Crossword (the answers are in cents)

Across

a. 6 dimes

b. 4 dimes + 3 pennies

c. 6 nickels

d. 2 quarters + 4 pennies

e. 3 quarters + 1 nickel

f. 12 pennies

g. 2 quarters + 1 nickel

h. 4 nickels + 2 pennies

i. 7 dimes + 5 pennies

j. 8 dimes + 2 nickels

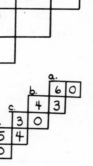

Answer

Down

a. 6 dimes + 3 pennies

b. 4 dimes

c. 6 nickels + 4 pennies

d. 5 dimes

e. 16 nickels + 2 pennies

f. 1 nickel + 1 dime

g. 5 dimes + 2 pennies

h. 1 quarter

i. 2 quarters + 2 dimes

j. 2 quarters + 8 nickels

How to Work Crossnumber Puzzles

Have you ever worked a crossword puzzle? Crossnumber puzzles are worked very much like crossword puzzles. Numbers are used instead of words. Practice on the little puzzle below.

Across	*Down*
(a) 6 + 9	(a) 9 x 2
(c) 3 ⟌ 96	(b) 30 x 4
(d) 70 +90	(c) 78 −42

First, work the problems marked across. Write your answers in the spaces across your drawing.

Next work the problems marked down. Write your answers in the spaces down your drawing.

If all your answers are correct, the numbers down will check the numbers already written across.

Your finished puzzle should look like this:

6 + 9 = 15. Write 15.

96 ÷ 3 = 32. Write 32.

70 + 90 = 160. Write 160.

2 × 9 = 18. Write 18.

4 × 30 = 120. Write 120.

78 − 42 = 36. This answer checks with the figures you have already written.

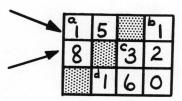

The Four Operations

Across

(a) 57 $\overline{)\,10{,}032}$

(d) 358 + 216 + 998 + 204 + 747

(h) 893 − 407   (i)   8 × 202

(j) 6 × 130   (k) 25 × 39

(l) 2,100 − 2,001

(m) 73 $\overline{)\,9{,}928}$

(o) 39 + 54 + 92 + 81 + 77 + 52

(p) 86 $\overline{)\,4{,}558}$ (q) 837 − 467

(r) 830 − 467   (s) 16 × 514

(t) 6,000 − 5,158

(u) 2,314 + 3,107 + 1,850 + 1,427

(v) 28 × 35

Down

(a) 2,436 + 1,248 + 6,322 + 4,784

(b) 39,456 − 31,567

(c) 12 × 55

(d) 4,837 + 5,192 + 3,925 + 7,981

(e) 43 × 132   (f)   7,000 − 6,78

(g) 93 $\overline{)\,3{,}348}$

(m) 4,184 + 3,879 + 4,987 + 5,998

(n) 3,972 + 5,864 + 4,839 + 8,645

(o) 33 × 113   (p) 16 × 353

(q) 29 $\overline{)\,9{,}454}$ (r) 46 $\overline{)\,17{,}894}$

(s) 925 − 837

Measures

Across

(a) A gross

(c) Inches in 9 feet

(e) Feet in 1 mile

(h) 4 decades plus 1 year

(j) Ounces in 3 pounds

(k) Nickels in $2.00

(l) Hours in 3 days

(n) Quarters in $7.00

(o) Quarts in 6 gallons

(p) Minutes in 1¼ hours

(q) Inches in ½ yard

(r) Area of square 7″ on a side

(t) Feet in 2 rods

(v) Digits whose sum equals the years in a decade

(x) Pounds in ⅕ ton

(y) Days in 15 weeks

Down

(a) Weeks in 2 years.

(b) 9 inches more than 1 yard

(c) Area of rectangle 5′ × 2′

(d) Yards in ½ mile

(f) Hours in 1 day

(g) Quarts in 11 pecks

(i) Area of land 72′ × 24′

(k) Digits whose sum equals the ounces in 1¼ pounds

(m) Months in 2 years

(n) 3 days less than a month

(q) Sq. in. in sq. ft.

(r) Minutes in ¾ hour

(s) Sq. ft. in 10 sq. yd.

(u) Days in 1 year

(v) Two and a half dozen

(w) 10½ pairs

Fractions

Across

(a) $12 \times 3\frac{1}{2}$ (c) $157\frac{1}{2} - 126\frac{2}{4}$

(e) $9 \times \frac{1}{2}$

(f) $2\frac{2}{3} + 2\frac{1}{6} + 1\frac{1}{2}$

(h) $3 - \frac{1}{6}$ (i) $21 \times 3\frac{2}{7}$

(j) $\frac{5}{6} \times 29$ (l) $10 \div \frac{4}{9}$

(m) $17\frac{1}{2} \div 2\frac{1}{3}$ (n) $5\frac{3}{5} + \frac{3}{10}$

(o) $21 \div \frac{3}{7}$ (p) $14 \div \frac{7}{12}$

(r) $4\frac{1}{2} \times 8\frac{3}{4}$ (s) $\frac{2}{3}$ of 10

Down

(a) $\frac{4}{5}$ of 55 (b) $1\frac{1}{8} + 1\frac{3}{8}$

(c) $8\frac{2}{3} \times 4\frac{1}{4}$ (d) $\frac{2}{3} \div \frac{1}{2}$

(g) $6\frac{1}{2} \times 3$ (h) $\frac{3}{4} + \frac{5}{6} +$

(i) $10 \times 6\frac{1}{5}$ (j) $9 \div \frac{1}{3}$

(k) $7\frac{1}{4} - 2\frac{3}{4}$ (l) $4\frac{1}{2} - 1\frac{3}{5}$

(n) $9\frac{1}{2} \times 6\frac{1}{4}$ (o) $12\frac{1}{4} \times 4$

(p) $39 \div 1\frac{1}{2}$

(q) $1\frac{1}{2} + 1\frac{1}{3} + 1\frac{5}{6}$

Decimal Fractions

a.	b		■	c	d	e	f.
g		■	h			.	
	■	i			.		
■	j			.			
k			.			■	■
l		.			■	m.	n
o	.			■	p.		
q.				■	r		

Across

(a) $.6 \times .7$

(g) $6.3 \overline{)453.6}$

(i) $\begin{array}{r} 32.64 \\ 40.88 \\ +\ 27.66 \\ \underline{19.35} \end{array}$

(k) $350.00 - 146.52$

(m) $.8 \overline{).72}$

(p) $9 \overline{)2.07}$

(r) $.27 \overline{)145.80}$

(c) $.13 \overline{)67.86}$

(h) $3.4 \overline{)969.68}$

(j) $\begin{array}{r} 64.516 \\ 40.872 \\ +\ 96.649 \\ \underline{57.008} \end{array}$

(l) $.6 \times 43.4$

(o) $7.92 - 2.66$

(q) $.7 \times .51$

Down

(a) $.5 \times 1.4$

(c) 7×82.92

(e) $\begin{array}{r} .73 \\ .54 \\ +\ .88 \\ \underline{.39} \end{array}$

(i) $\begin{array}{r} 22.28 \\ 63.72 \\ +\ 29.51 \\ \underline{37.74} \end{array}$

(m) $20.09 - 19.85$

(n) $.21 \overline{)195.3}$

(b) $.4 \overline{)16.8}$

(d) $.03 \times 836$

(f) $.5 \times .47$

(h) 3.7×61.91

(j) $.02 \overline{)4.126}$

(k) $.7 \overline{)157.5}$

(p) $25 \overline{)12.5}$

.	4	2	■	5	2	2	.
7	2	■	2	8	5	.	2
0	■	1	2	0	.	5	3
■	2	5	9	.	0	4	5
2	0	3	.	4	8	■	■
2	6	.	0	4	■	.	9
5	.	2	6	■	.	2	3
.	3	5	7	■	5	4	0

Problems

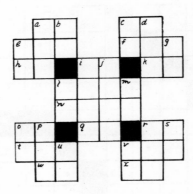

Across

(a) Jack bought ¾ pound of peanuts at 48 cents a pound. How much change should he receive from a half dollar?

(c) Perimeter of a rectangle 11 inches by 8 inches.

(e) Tom's father earns $12 a day. Last month he worked 26¼ days. What was his total pay?

(f) 6 per cent of $7,300 = ■

(h) Apples are 3 for 10 cents. How many can Sue buy for $1.20?

(i) If 5 servings can be made from a quart of ice cream, how many gallons should the club buy for 240 people?

(k) How many ¾ in. ribbons can be cut from 1½ yd. of silk?

(l) In an election for mayor, 8,078 votes were cast. Mr. Sands received 3,160 votes; Mr. Bower, 1,975 votes; and Mr. Bell, the rest. How many votes did Mr. Bell get?

(n) Mrs. Wilson withdrew ⅘ of her money from the bank. If she had $260 left in the bank, how much money did she have at first?

(o) 2,775 ÷ 75 = ■

(q) A candymaker put 400 pounds of fudge in an equal number of 1-pound, 2-pound, and 5-pound bags. How many 1-pound bags did he make?

(r) $1,945 - 1,882 = $ ■   (t) $3,744 \div 6\frac{1}{2} = $ ■

(v) If ⅚ of a roll of carpeting is worth $160, what is a whole roll worth?

(w) What is the sum of the million's digit and the thousand's digit in 98,527,136?

(x) In one year, Mr. Hamilton drove his car 4,836 miles. How many miles a week did he average?

Down

(a) Square inches in rectangle 14½″ by 8″.

(b) Inches in 3¾ feet.   (c) $578 \div 17 = $ ■

(d) $30,250 - 29,413 = $ ■   (e) Feet in 2 rods.

(g) Mr. Levi is driving from Albany to Buffalo, a distance of 335 miles. He averages 46 miles an hour for 5½ hours. How far is he from Buffalo?

(i) Dick was born in 1942 and is 7 years younger than Harry. When was Harry born?

(j) Add MCDLII and CMXLVIII.

(l) Center High School gym had 420 seats; ⅘ are reserved for Center students; ¾ of the remainder, for the visiting school. How many seats are not reserved?

(m) Cost of 9 feet by 12 feet rug at $2.50 a square yard.

(o) If 48 chickens cost $120, how much are 14 chickens?

(p) Subtract DXVI from MCLXXXVII.

(r) $1,248 - 555 = $ ■

(s) Farmer Brown raised 80 chickens. He sold 60 per cent of them. How many did he have left?

(u) A man bought an estate for $15,000. If the buildings are worth $2,650 and the estate contains 190 acres, what did he pay per acre for the land?

(v) Mr. Wells paid $7.35 for flour, $24 for a plough, and 9.5 cents a pound for 30 pounds of sugar. How many bushels of potatoes at $1.80 a bushel will pay his bill?

Puzzle

¹1	²2	³5		⁴4	⁵8
⁶2	⁷0	⁸6	⁹7		¹⁰4
	¹¹0			¹²1	
¹³2		¹⁴1	¹⁵2	¹⁶5	¹⁷1
¹⁸1	¹⁹8		²⁰0	²¹0	²²0

Across

1. 25 × 5
4. 4 tens plus 8 ones
6. 67 more than 4,000 ÷ 2
14. one thousand, two hundred, fifty-one
18. 6 yards = ____ ft.
20. a number that when multiplied always yields the product zero

Down

1. 4 × 8 − 8 ÷ 2
2. 2 × 10 × 10
3. four, fourteen times
5. 7 ft. = ____ in.
12. 750 ÷ 5
13. 12 × 8 − ____ = 75
15. ⅝ of a yard = ____ in.
16. 2,500 ÷ 50
17. Even number less than 15 and is divisible by 5

Problems

a	b			c	d	e		f	g	h
i			j			k			l	
		m			●		n			
	o		●			p	●		q	
r					s				t	
u		●					v●			
w			x	y		z	A			
	B		●			C	●			
D		E			F●					G
H	I		J						K	
L				M			N			

Across

(a)   What is the perimeter of a rectangle whose sides measure 27 and 28?

(c).   Find the divisor when the quotient is 23 and the dividend is 3,726.

(f)   How many square feet are in 15 square yards?

(i)   What is the number of acres in a rectangular field 64 rods long and 60 rods wide?

(j)   MDCCCXXXIV multiplied by 6.

(l)   What is the remainder when 6,640 is divided by 83?

(m)   .198 more than 2.6×62.26.

(o)   Find the perimeter of a triangle whose sides are 2.4, 3.8, and 4.6.

(p)   ⅓ of (?) = 1.42.

(r)   A factory employs 350 men at $1.375 per hour. What is the payroll for a work week of 40 hours?

(s)   One thousand eighty more than eighty-three thousand four hundred thirty-two.

(u)   Round off 51.675 to the nearest whole number.

(v) $27.8 \overline{)1.668}$

(w)   Find the minuend when the difference is 5,366 and the subtrahend in 18,309.

(z)   What is the product of 144 and 162?

(B)   Perimeter of square with side 7.4 inches long.

(C) $1.2 \times (?) = 2.136.$ (E) $44.1 \times 11.25 = \blacksquare$

(H)   ⅓ the area of rectangle with sides 14 and 9.

(J) $(?) \div 3\frac{1}{2} = 7,664.$ (K) $7\frac{1}{2} \times {}^{16}\!/_5 = \blacksquare$

(L)   10 ft. more than ⅙ mi.

(M)   Inches in 3 yards 2 feet 8 inches.

(N) $15 - {}^{13}\!/_3 = \blacksquare$

Down

(a)   132 less than 7 × 36.

(c)   Seconds in 3 hr. 8 min.

(e)   What is the quotient when 601.44 is divided by .03?

(g)   One fourth the difference between 390 and 238.

(h)   172 more than 328.

(j)   Average of 10.6, 17.3, 18.5, 19.6.

(k)   90.8 less than 138.2.

(m)   35.293 + 20.826 + 18.190 + 28.385.

(n)   Express $425\frac{3}{8}$ as a decimal.

(o)   What is the number of thousands in nineteen million two hundred thirty-two thousand?

(q)   146 × 418 = ■

(t)   25 per cent of (?) = 67.

(y)   The sum of the digits of this number is the number of ounces in 1.5 pounds.

(z)   Inches in ⅓ mile.

(D)   Difference between 502 and 354.

(F)   65.52 ÷ 78 = ■

(I) $2\frac{5}{12}$ = ?/12.

(b)   8 per cent of 175.

(d) $\frac{3}{5}$ = (?) per cent.

(r)   217 + 814 – 879 = ■

(x)   (?) ÷ 100 = .0792.

(A)   1,000 × (?) = 3,240.

(G)   2 × 7⅓ = ■

(K)   (?) per cent of 25 = 5.

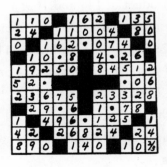

Crossword Puzzle with Mathematical Terms

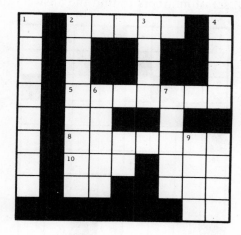

Across

2. Sets having no elements.
5. What must be done to sell material or ribbon.
8. To make null.
10. Assessment to support the government.

Down

1. Take away by deducing.
2. Individual objects of the set.
3. Links
4. Foundation
6. Identical in mathematical values.
7. A joining together.
9. The fourth in a set.

Answers

Across

2. Empty
5. Measure
8. Nullify
10. Tax

Down

1. Subtract
2. Elements
3. Ties
4. Base
6. Equal
7. Union
9. Four

Crossnumber Puzzle

Add the given set of numbers to find the answers to the puzzle.

Across

1. 4,000; 525; 610
4. 522; 71
7. 195; 36
8. 6,321; 2,100; 500
9. 22; 23
10. 3,329; 4,470
11. 310, 321; 100; 400
13. 11,576; 2,510
14. 54, 221, 000; 201,017; 100
15. 520, 200; 43, 200
16. 6,521; 1,600
17. 101; 87
19. 5,115; 900

Down

1. 4,431; 810
2. 95; 40
3. 25; 6
4. 59,000,000; 986,000; 101
5. 7,892; 1,400
6. 28; 3
8. 560,000; 310,820
10. 6,952,411; 150,000
11. 2,541,699; 901,502
12. 951,321; 223,501
13. 52,650; 93,511
14. 451;107
15. 07; 51

21. 60; 12
22. 210; 01
23. 2,221; 901

18. 771; 101
19. 60; 01
20. 21; 32
21. 59; 13

Answers

Across

1. 5,135
4. 593
7. 231
8. 8,921
9. 45
10. 7,799
11. 310,821
13. 14,086
14. 54,422,117
15. 563,400
16. 8,121
17. 188
19. 6,015
21. 72
22. 211
23. 3,122

Down

1. 5,241
2. 135
3. 31
4. 59,986,101
5. 9,292
6. 31
8. 870,820
10. 7,102,411
11. 3,443,201
12. 1,174,822
13. 146,161
14. 558
15. 58
18. 872
19. 61
20. 53
21. 72

Crossnumber Puzzle

Find a way to complete this crossnumber puzzle. Write in the numbers from 1-13 inclusive, in the empty boxes. They must total the exact amount shown at the ends of the 11 rows.

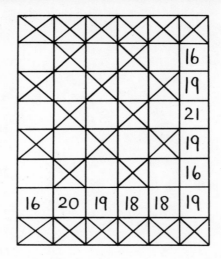

Answers across from the top:
3, 8, 5, 7, 12, 9, 1, 11, 13, 6, 4, 10, 2.

Crossnumber Puzzle

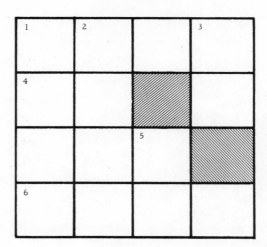

Across

1. First 4 even numbers
4. 96 − 5
6. 4,001 + 1,299

Down

1. 5,000 − 2,095
2. 8,246 ÷ 2
3. 8 × 10
5. 2 × 5

Answers

Across	Down
1. 2,468	1. 2,905
4. 91	2. 4,123
6. 5,300	3. 80
	5. 10

Crossnumeral Puzzle

Across

(a) 1,140 + 1,149 = n

(e) 2,001 − 150 = n

(i) Round 208 to the nearest 10

(j) Nine twelves = n

(k) 2,188 + one hundred seven = n

(m) Eight hundred tens = n

(n) The number of nines in eighteen = n

(o) (51,000 + 16,000) − 1,230 = n

(q) The number of sevens in zero = n

(r) One hundred, one ten and one seven = n

(s) The number of eights in fifty-six = n

(t) (60,000 − 1,000) + 300 + 53 = n

(v) The number of sixes in forty-two = n

(w) Three thousand less five tens = n

(y) Twenty five hundred ninety-eight plus thirty seven hundred forty-seven = n

(A) (18 ÷ 2) + (21 ÷ 3) + 88 = n

Down

(a) 2,000 + 200 + 20 + 2 = n

(b) 100 + 100 + 10 + 2 = n

(c) 10,000 = 1,904 + n, n = ?

(d) The largest one digit number = n

(e) The number of eights in eight = n

(f) Eighty-one hundreds = n

(g) Two zero four and 296 = n

(h) Eighteen hundred = n

(l) 18,708 + 36,482 = n

(m) 87 thousands + 75 tens + 6 = n

(p) 712 < n ■ <714

(s) Twelve hundred twelve more than six thousand = n

(t) 8,810 − 3,268 = n

(u) 7,285 = 3,929 + n, n = ?

(v) Seven hundred fifty tens = n

(x) Number of nines in 8,109 = n

(z) The number of eights in thirty-two a hundred times = n

Across

(B) One hundred fives = n

(C) Six eights + the number
of sixes in thirty-six +
two thousand sixty-nine
= n

(D) The number of sevens in
sixty-three, plus the
number of nines in forty-
five, plus five thousand
five hundred eighty-six =
n

Crossnumeral Puzzle

Across

(1) $(90 \times 70) + 1 = n$

(4) $(90 \times 90) + (90 \times 8) = n$

(7) $40 \times 93 = n$

(8) $840 - 321 = n$

(9) $\$1.73 - \$1.67 = n$

(10) $10 \div 5 = n$

(11) $80 \times 73 = n$

(12) $364 - 265 = n$

(14) $1,943 - 89 = n$

(16) $n \div 8 = 7, n = ?$

(18) $435 + 654 + 78 = n$

(20) $n \div 9 = 4, n = ?$

(22) $6 \times 50 = n$

(23) 420 tens $= n$

(24) $n \div 50 = 12, n = ?$

(25) $n \times 6 = 48, n = ?$

(28) 36 threes $= n$

(30) six nines $= n$

(31) $n \times 4 = 320, n = ?$

(32) $6,675 \times 60 = n$

Down

(1) $90 \times 70 = n$

(2) $40 \times 94 = n$

(3) $53,949 + 49,038 = n$

(4) $(9 \times 90) + (9 \times 5) = n$

(5) $20 \times 409 = n$

(6) 42 sevens $= n$

(13) $(3 \times 30) + 5 = n$

(14) $20 \times 80 = n$

(15) $6 \times (9 \times 8) = n$

(16) $n \times 6 = 30, n = ?$

(17) $n \div 7 = 9, n = ?$

(18) $378 \times 6 \times 6 = n$

(19) 20 fives $= n$

(21) 76 eights $= n$

(23) $70 \times 60 = n$

(26) 54 tens $= n$

(27) $8 \times 0 = n$

(28) $n \times 7 = 98, n = ?$

(29) $n \times 8 = 640, n = ?$

(30) 10 fives $= n$

(33) $n \times 12 = 60, n = ?$

Crossword Puzzle

Measurement

Across

1. 2 _____ equal 1 pint.
5. Table _____ .
8. 24 hours equal 1 _____ .
9. You need _____ hours of sleep.
11. Opposite of on is _____ .
13. Abbreviation for Saturday.
16. 24 equals _____ dozen.
17. A _____ tells time.
20. _____ 0 _____ are nice.
21. 60 minutes equal one _____ .
23. 100 pennies equal a _____ .
25. And minus d _____ .
26. Opposite of a.m. _____ .
28. 5 pennies equal a _____ .
30. Opposite of solid is _____ .
32. This sign (plus) means _____ .
34. Tell _____ the time.
35. ¼ + ¼ + ¼ + ¼ equal 1 _____ on a ruler.
36. 1 _____ equals one cent.
37. Watches tell _____ .
39. 12 months equal 1 _____ .
41. Bill knows his math. _____ is smart.
42. Find the _____ : 12 plus 12 plus 12 equals 2 dozen.
43. 25 cents equals 1 _____ .

Down

1. 4 o' _____ .
2. 3:30 equals half _____ three.
3. 4 quarts equal 1 _____ .
4. _____ o'clock equals 10 p.m.
6. ¼ bushel equals 1 _____ .
7. One half _____ one gallon equals 2 quarts.
10. ½ of 1 pint equals 1 _____ _____ . (2 words)
11. Opposite of off equals _____ .
12. _____ quarts equal 1 gallon.
14. 7 days equal _____ _____ . (2 words)
15. I like _____ spend money.
18. 1 _____ equals ½ pint or ¼ quart.
19. February equals 1 _____ .
20. 36 inches equals 1 _____ .
21. A _____ dollar equals 50 cents.
22. 12 inches are on 1 _____ .
24. 10 cents equals 1 _____ .
27. Name for dollars and cents.
29. 2 nickels equal 10 _____ .
31. 1 _____ equals 2 pints or 4 cups.
33. March 28, 1968 is today's _____ .
35. Contraction of I am is _____ .
38. There are 60 seconds _____ one minute.
40. _____ 12:00 both hands are on the 12.

Across

32. Watches tell _____.
34. 12 months equals 1 _____.
36. Bill knows his math. _____ is smart.
37. Find the _____ : 12 plus 12 plus 12 plus 12 equals 3 dozen.
38. 25 cents equals 1 _____.
39. Water is a _____.

Down

25. 2 nickels equals 10 _____.
26. 1 _____ equals 2 pints or 4 cups.
29. Abbreviation for I am: _____.
30. March 28, 1968 is today's _____.
33. There are 60 seconds _____ 1 minute.
35. _____ 12:00 both hands are on the 12.

Answers With this activity the teacher may include a vocabulary list for the children to choose their answers from.

Across

1. Cups	27. Add
5. Spoon	28. Me
7. Day	29. Inch
8. Eight	31. Penny
9. Off	32. Time
10. Sat.	34. Year
14. Two	36. He
15. Clock	37. Sum
18. You	38. Quarter
19. Hour	39. Liquid
20. Dollar	
23. p.m.	
24. Nickel	

Down

1. Clock	21. Dime
2. Past	22. Ruler
3. Gallon	25. Cents
4. Ten	26. Quart
6a. Peck	29. I'm
6. Of	30. Date
9. On	33. In
11. A week	35. At
12. To	
13. Half pint	
16. Cup	
17. Month	
18. Yard	
19. Half	

4

Individual and Group Games

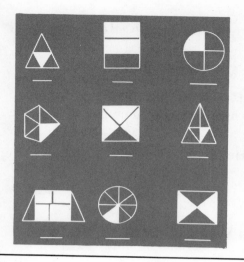
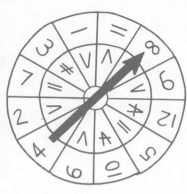

Domino Magic

Ask someone to choose any domino without a blank from a box of dominoes. Then ask him to do these things:

1. Multiply one of the numbers on his domino by 5.
2. Add 7 to the result.
3. Multiply the sum by 2.
4. Add the other number on his domino.
5. Tell you his answer.

Knowing his answer, you can tell him the two numbers on his domino.

Suppose he chooses the 6:3 domino.

He multiplies one of the numbers by 5.	He adds 7 to the result.	He multiplies the sum by 2.

$$
\begin{array}{r} 6 \\ \times\ 5 \\ \hline 30 \end{array}
\qquad
\begin{array}{r} 30 \\ +\ 7 \\ \hline 37 \end{array}
\qquad
\begin{array}{r} 37 \\ \times\ 2 \\ \hline 74 \end{array}
$$

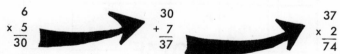

He adds the other number on his domino.

He tells you his answer is 77.

$$
\begin{array}{r} 74 \\ +\ 3 \\ \hline 77 \end{array}
$$

77

Answer

You subtract 14 from his answer. The result is a two-figure number made up of the two numbers on the domino chosen at the start.

$$\begin{array}{r} 77 \\ -14 \\ \hline 63 \end{array}$$ (He chose the 6:3 domino.)

Jump a Winner Home

This game is played by two teams. Subscripts are to be used as divisors, the children are to give only the remainders as answers. Start at upper left-hand corner, the player for the first team starting. If pupil gives correct answer he jumps four spaces. The starting player for the next team starts with numeral to right of the first team's starting space. If he makes correct answer his team jumps four spaces. The play continues like this with correct answers. When an incorrect answer is given pupils must move back three spaces and are to follow the arrows. The first team to move into Home is the winner of the game.

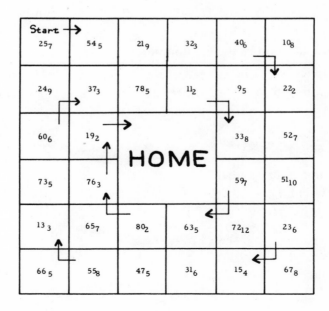

Divide to Get Home

This game provides practice in short division with remainders. Write the numbers 2 to 9 three times on 24 small cards. Two or three people may play at once and each person has his own marker. To begin, the player turns over the first card of the deck of one-digit numbers. Using short division, he is to divide the number by the numeral under his market by this one-digit number. The rules concerning movement of markets for correct and incorrect answers are the same as in the preceding game.

3001	659	484	853	309	4021
813	1236	715	151	449	362
5162	418	HOME		2501	214
999	789			569	675
422	989	620	815	781	1216
2847	974	297	651	452	START 516

Number Checkers

Number checkers is played on a 7½″ × 12″ board which may be made of cardboard. Each player will need a number of numerals equal to twice the sum being studied. This game is to gain proficiency in addition. If the addition facts of 9 are being studied, each student will need 18 numerals or two 1's, two 8's, two 2's, two 7's, two 3's, two 6's, two 4's, and four 5's.

By agreement each child may arrange either his own numerals on the board any way he wishes or those of his opponent. A move may be made upwards, downwards, sideways, or diagonally, and only one square at a time. The object is to place one numeral on another to total the agreed upon sum, e.g. 9. The cards may be turned over or removed from the board. If a numeral cannot be placed on another to total 9, it may be moved to an adjoining blank space in preparation for a later move. The person getting nine totals of 9 wins.

9	7	3	4	L	5
8	1	5	8	7	4
3	5	5	1	L	9
3	4	8	6	2	5
6	7	1	5	4	3
5	2	1	8	5	7

Reducing Fractions

Do these simple examples below very carefully. Then connect the like number of dots in the order that they appear in your answers. Read downward to produce a complete picture.

1. $\frac{4}{8}$ = $\frac{1}{2}$

2. $\frac{3}{12}$ =

3. $\frac{2}{6}$ =

4. $\frac{2}{10}$ =

5. $\frac{2}{12}$ =

6. $\frac{5}{35}$ =

7. $\frac{4}{6}$ =

8. $\frac{2}{18}$ =

9. $\frac{10}{12}$ =

10. $\frac{16}{20}$ =

11. $\frac{3}{24}$ =

12. $\frac{3}{42}$ =

13. $\frac{32}{36}$ =

14. $\frac{2}{32}$ =

15. $\frac{10}{16}$ =

16. $\frac{12}{28}$ =

17. $\frac{16}{36}$ =

18. $\frac{21}{24}$ =

19. $\frac{12}{16}$ =

20. $\frac{9}{15}$ =

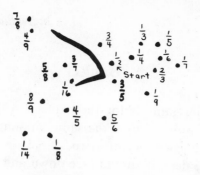

Bingo with Roman Numerals

In this particular game, the actual purpose is reinforcement of the Roman numeral concept. The children have learned their numerals sufficiently and are able to identify them accurately and quickly. Thus, the reader says the numbers in *ARABIC*, and the students (who all have cards similar to the one here) seek the Roman numeral equivalent.

R	O	M	A	N
III	IV	X	VIII	U
M	C	IV	XII	M
IX	XIX	FREE	XCI	E
XXV	XD	MCML	LXVI	R
XVIII	IX	LXX	V	A
XXXIII	XLIX	XXVIII	VI	L
LXXII	II	XIII	II	S

Banker

The idea of the game is for the players to realize that various combinations of money equal the same amount. Shuffle the cards and deal five to each player (two, three or four people). The remainder of the deck is spread face down and is called the Bank. After the deal each player removes all pairs or equals from his hand and places them face down on the table.

The dealer asks any player for a card that matches one in his hand. If the player he asked has that card he must give it up. The matched pair is removed from his hand and added to the pile of pairs. If the player doesn't have the card asked for, he tells the dealer to ask another player or go to the Bank. If he draws a card from the Bank and it is the one he needed, he asks another player for a second card.

If he can't find a match, the person on his right has a turn. The game continues until one of the players has no remaining cards. The player with the most pairs is the bank president and winner. A total of 34 cards is used for the game.

Card examples may include:

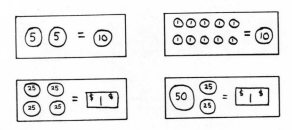

Clock Base System

Can you identify the base system used for this clock?

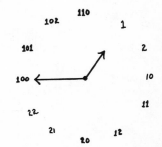

Category Quick

Materials: A blank card headed with six categories as shown below is given to each player. The game is designed for two or four players.

Directions: The players have 15 minutes to fill their cards by writing the name of one object or term used in talking about or working with that category. Examples are written on the card shown below. Categories may be changed to topics currently being taught in the classroom.

Scoring: Answers are compared orally. Under each category, 5 points is scored for an original answer. 1 point is scored for a duplicate answer. Total number of possible points for one game is 180. After answers are compared and scores are tallied the player scoring the most points wins.

Geometric Shapes	Numbers	Measurement	Money	Sets	Parts of a Problem
triangle	nine	ton	quarter	union	addend
polygon	fifty	ounce	dollar	disjoint	sum
circle	two	foot	penny	null	product
square	eighteen	bushel	dime	intersect	minuend
rectangle	one hundred	pound	nickel	subset	divisor
octagon	two thousand	inch	half dollar	equivalent	dividend

Matching

Do the first problem in Column 1. Then find the problems in Columns II and III that make the same statement in another way, and solve those. Do the same for all the problems.

I	II	III
A. (6 + 7) + 3 =	A. (16 + 4) + 18 =	A. 38 + (25 + 75) =
B. 38 + 100 =	B. 5 X (1+1+1) =	B. 6 + 10 =
C. 3 X (2 + 4) =	C. (10 X 4) + (10 X 3) =	C. (3 X 2) + (3 X 4) =
D. 20 + 18 =	D. 6 + (7 + 3) =	D. 16 + (4 + 18) =
E. 5 + 5 + 5 =	E. (38 + 25) + 75 =	E. 5 X 3 =
F. 10 X (4 + 3) =	F. 6 X 3 =	F. 10 X 7 =

	Solutions				
A.	16	D.	16	B.	16
B.	138	E.	138	A.	138
C.	18	F.	18	C.	18
D.	38	A.	38	D.	38
E.	15	B.	15	E.	15
F.	70	C.	70	F.	70

Basketball Statistics

Form basketball teams of five students each. Group them according to deficiency needs, re the current arithmetic unit. Each teams gets about 50 examples written on separate strips of durable material, each strip indicating the particular move in basketball that it represents. Each child selects a strip at random. If he cannot solve it, he puts it aside and takes another. The whole team tries to do the unsolved ones after all the other examples are finished. Each child works as many as he can and must prove each. A score is kept that describes each individual move and the record of the team as a whole. The teams are called by the names they select for themselves.

TIGERS	Field Goals		Free Throws		Totals		Percentages to nearest whole
	Tried	Scored	Tried	Scored	Tried	Scored	
Bob	111	11	11	1	5	3	3/5, 60%
John	1111	1111	1	1	5	5	5/5, 100%
Jack	11	11	111	0	5	2	2/5, 40%
Ed	11111	1111	0	0	5	4	4/5, 80%
Sam	1111	0	1	1	5	1	1/5, 20%
Team	11	1	1	1	3	2	2/3, 67%
Total	20	13	8	4	28	17	17/28, 61%

Team scores are compared and the highest wins. These may be carried over to the next unit in a "tournament." The children may each keep a personal record, which is kept private.

Barrel of Monkeys Counting Game

Using the commercial game equipment, "Barrel of Monkeys," name the monkey figures by color for any value you choose: red - 2 points, blue - 4 points, and yellow - 6 points. As the children hook the monkeys together, they add their score. The highest scorer takes first turn in the next game.

Calendar Base 9

Have the students make a calendar in base 9. Show them a present day calendar and then ask them how a calendar would have looked in a civilization that used base 9.

SEPTEMBER

SUN.	MON.	TUES.	WED.	THURS.	FRI.	SAT.
				1	2	3
4	5	6	7	8	10	11
12	13	14	15	16	17	18
20	21	22	23	24	25	26
27	28	30	31	32	33	

Blast-Off

Sketch a rocket and numbers on the blackboard. Numbers may be selected as to needs of the students. See how many can get the rocket into orbit by giving the correct sums to all combinations. Change the number of the rocket's nose as the combinations are learned. This can also be used for multiplication facts.

Spin and Count

Make a cardboard circle and paste groups of small buttons, shells, etc., on it—putting a number in each of 12 divisions. Make a division with 1, then 2, etc., up to 10 or 12. Cut out an arrow and attach it to the center of the circle with a brad. Let each child spin his own pointer and count the number of objects which the point indicates. Write the number down and spin again. Count and write the number down. Add the numbers of objects together and put the total down. This can be used for column addition also.

Making a Tree

Draw the trunk of a tree on a chalkboard, with the number 10 on it. The pupils draw limbs as they give the answers to addition or subtraction combinations named by the teacher. For example, teacher says, "Six plus what equals ten?" The first child to say "four" draws the limb and writes " 6 + 4 " on it. Any suitable number may be written on the trunk, as practice is needed.

Telephone

Each pupil is given a number. The teacher then says, "I am calling 2 and 4" (or any combination, addition or subtraction, as appropriate). The pupil who has the number 6 (if addition, 2 if subtraction) answers, "This is 6." The game continues in like manner.

Who'll Be the Teacher

Combinations being studied are written on cards (approximately 3 x 5 inches in size). These are shuffled, and the teacher starts by showing a card and calling on a pupil for the answer. A correct answer is rewarded by the answerer being handed the card. The pupil holding the most cards when the stack has been used becomes the "Teacher" for the next game.

Show Me Kit

At the beginning of the school year, give each child a 6 x 9 inch envelope. Staple a 1 inch pocket to the longer side. The child is also given eleven cards, 2 x 3 inches in size. On the cards he writes the digits from 0 to 9 and an extra 1. The cards are kept in the envelope and are used for the entire year. They are placed on the child's desk in the correct order so they can be found quickly. When the teacher asks: "How many are 9 + 8," the child places the correct answer in his pocket so that the numbers show and holds it against his chest until the teacher says, "Show me." During the year, we also make ½, ¼, hundreds, tens, ones, etc. This activity allows all the pupils to respond.

The Elephant Never Forgets

This idea is a good teaching aid. The shape of an elephant is cut out of cardboard, and hung in a convenient place. A saddle cloth is represented by a paper flap. Underneath this is a different flap which is concealed each morning. The children lift up the flap when they wish, and try to memorize the fact. Towards the end of the school day, the teacher asks every child to write down that day's fact.

Number Spelldown

To give children more practice in changing tens into ones and ones into tens, and in thinking of numbers in these terms, let them have a spelldown in the manner described below. Let the children first number off with the odds on one team and the evens on another. Start the game by having the leader of one side ask the leader of the other to change 5 tens, 16 ones into its correct numerical form (66). If the opposing member does so correctly, it would be his turn to ask the next person in the first team to change a group of tens and some ones into their numerical form. When a player misses, he must sit down and give the next member on the opposite side a chance to answer. The child who remains standing at the end is the winner. The game may also be played by giving a number (34) and asking that it be changed to tens and ones in such a way that the ones number will be more than 9. It may be advisable at first for the teacher to call out the numbers, as "6 tens and 18 ones," "7 tens and 21 ones,"etc. This game can also be adapted to numbers of three figures by using such combinations as "3 hundreds, 14 tens, 8 ones."

Show Me Shapes Game

To make sure the children know circles, rectangles, squares, and triangles, ask them to cut a variety of sizes and shapes from scraps of colored paper. Let your children use them to create interesting and imaginative figures by pasting them on black or white paper. Then let them tell how many of each shape they have used to make the figures. Another method is to see how quickly each child can hold up a triangle, circle, square, and rectangle. They also like to play Show Me by calling on someone to touch something that is a circle, square, or rectangle.

Ladder Game

A number of ladders should be drawn on the blackboard and combinations placed on the rungs. Each ladder has the same combinations but they are arranged in different orders. A child stands close to each ladder and is told to climb to the top as fast as he can without falling off (making a mistake). Each child has a piece of chalk and writes down the results at the side of the rungs as he climbs the ladder. The child who gets to the top first is the winner.

Guessing — Place Value

Students play this game in pairs. Each thinks of a three (or four, etc.) digit number and records the number of blank spaces needed to fill in the correct number. As an example, for a three digit: - - -. For each "yes" answer a student gets from a guess, he gets another guess. For a "no" answer, the other student takes his turn at guessing.

Legal guesses: "Do you have a certain digit in your number (like 3)?
                   "Is this digit in a certain position (middle, last, etc.)?

The first student that succeeds in writing down the other's number wins.

Drop the Cork

Materials needed are an empty coffee can and a supply of corks. Place a two-figure or three-figure number on the top of each cork. Let each child have several turns at dropping corks in the can. As soon as he has two in the can, have him add the numbers. The player with the most number of corks and the highest total wins.

The Product Is

Provide each group of four players with a deck of cards from which the face cards have been removed. The dealer deals each player one card face up. Then he turns up the remaining cards in the center of the playing area, one at a time. The first player who can call out "The Product Is..." and give the product of his card and the center card, claims the card. He receives a new card, face up, and the game continues. The player with the most cards at the end of playing is the winner. Regroup the winners for a new game, and form new groups with the other three players.

Pick Your Operation

Prepare cards for four columns containing a problem on one side and the operation used on the other side. The first column should be easy with the next three becoming more difficult. The first column counts 5 points, second 10 points, the third 15 points, and the fourth 20 points. The child chooses a column card and answers it. The child with the highest number of points wins.

Geometric Math

Make up any work sheet with perhaps 25 problems spaced evenly over a $8\frac{1}{2} \times 11$ inch paper. Ask each child to cut up his work sheet into at least 5 geometric shapes and work only those problems found in each shape. The object is to work as many problems as possible while learning the new shapes, too.

Solutions Up!

Choose five people to begin the game. They make up five problems on five cards. The rest of the class put their heads on their desks as the five circulate around the room. The five leave their cards at five desks and return to the front of the room. The children then raise their heads and if they find a card on their desk, they work it as quickly as possible. If a child is having trouble working his problems, he raises his hand and the child who left the card with him goes to the desk and helps him. When "solutions up" is called the five go to the board and show their work. The entire process is repeated.

Round Arithmetic

The class or group arranges their desks in a circle. A problem is passed around the circle and each person solves it. If everyone is able to work that problem quickly, begin another problem and gradually another. Whoever has two problems at one time must drop out of the game. They must remain out for one minute. After this time, they may re-enter. This is a good drill exercise.

Shadow Number Game

In learning number sequence, boys and girls could construct the numbers from 1-10 or how many in the class out of construction colored paper and put them on popsicle sticks. Each child holds a number. A child is chosen to bring his numbers behind the shadow stage. The numbers which precede and follow that number are to come behind the shadow stage, too.

Answer Catcher

A child is chosen, he thinks of a problem, and he tells the teacher. The teacher then tells the rest of the children, who are divided into four groups, three numbers and the correct answer. The group with the correct answer is not aware of it. The chosen child then tells the others his problem and the group with the correct answer attempts to run past the child who called the problem or the answer catcher. The child who caught the most answers is the winner.

What's the Next Number?

Two teams are chosen by two captains and are arranged in a circle with the members of each team being placed between the members of the other team. The captains stand in the center. Beginning in opposite directions, they ask the first person on their teams to begin saying the numbers in sequence or by 5's or any sequence. The first captain who makes the complete circuit of his team wins.

They Add to Ten

Use a regular deck of cards and remove all face cards. Leave the aces in the deck. Aces have a value of one, the rest of the cards have face value.
Number of players: four

Deal:	Deal three cards to each player, put the rest of the deck in the center of the table face down.
Object:	Add face values of the cards to get "ten"; any number of cards may be used to get the desired sum.

Method: First player, the person sitting to the left of the dealer, draws a card from the deck. If he can get a sum of "ten" he draws again, and keeps drawing from the deck until he cannot get the desired sum of "ten." This continues, in a clockwise direction, until all the cards in the deck are gone or until a player uses all his cards by adding them up to "ten."

Winner: The first player to get rid of all his cards or the player with the smallest sum in his hand when they run out of cards in the deck.

Teen Pictures

In order to learn the teen numbers (11 to 19), have two children work together. Let one drop a number of objects (buttons, corks, jacks) on the table. When there are more than ten objects, have the child draw a circle with string around the group of ten. Then note the ones left over. He should be able to write the teen number immediately.

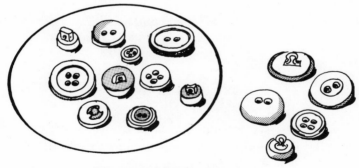

Dog Show Weights

These dogs have to be weighed before they enter the dog show.

1. How many pounds must the Scottie gain to weigh as much as the Boxer?

2. The weight of which two dogs equals the weight of which one dog?

3. How much more does the Great Dane weigh than the Boxer?

4. Some of the dogs were on the scales together. The scales read 140 pounds. The Fox Terrier got off and the Schnauzer got on. What did the scale read then?

Answers

1. 50

2. Fox Terrier and Pekingese = Scottie

3. 20 pounds

4. 155 pounds

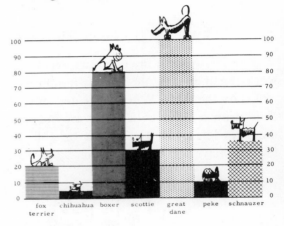

Cards in Ten

Procedure: The sixteen number cards are to be arranged so that the numbers in each column, each row, and each diagonal will total ten.

Solution:

1	1	1	1
2	2	2	2
3	3	3	3
4	4	4	4

- - - - - - - - - - - - - - - - - - - -

1	4	2	3
3	2	4	1
4	1	3	2
2	3	1	4

Musical Equations

Using the following, complete the equations:

$$\circ = 1 \qquad \text{d} = \tfrac{1}{2} \qquad \text{♩} = \tfrac{1}{4} \qquad ♪ = \tfrac{1}{8}$$

d × ♩ =

♪ + ♪ =

d ÷ ♪ =

♩ ÷ d =

∘ × ♪ =

∘ ÷ d =

d ÷ ♪ =

♪ ÷ d =

Answers:

⅛, ¼, 4, ½, ⅛, 2, 4, ¼

Bingo

A group of bingo cards with measurement words, symbols, or numerals can be made by the teacher. As one student draws a card with a measurement problem on it, the other students will work the problem out and find the answer on their cards.

The problems may be a mixture of definitions, pictures, or numeral problems.

$1.00	24hours	liquid	pennies
nickel	2:00am	money	gallon
quart	ruler	12inches	penny
pint	&	yard	foot
week	hour	month	$

Guess the Rule

Read the following example to the children and see if they can guess the rule and determine the number pattern:

When Mary said 5, Jim said 3

When Mary said 7, Jim said 5

When Mary said 8, Jim said 6

When Mary said 12, Jim said 10

What rule was Jim using?   *Answer:*   subtraction of 2

Now try this one:

When Kathy said 7, Dick said 21

When Kathy said 3, Dick said 9

When Kathy said 9, Dick said 27

When Kathy said 4, Dick said ? (12)

Answer: multiplication by 3

You can do this with fractions, decimals, and in all of the operations. The first child to guess the answer then makes up his own game.

Taxi

One child stands next to his desk while another child stands next to him in the aisle. The teacher flashes a card containing a problem of addition, multiplication, subtraction, division, measurement, Roman numerals, or any other topic the teacher has chosen. The object of the game is to be the first person to answer the problem correctly. The child that answers incorrectly must take his seat. The child that answered correctly first moves back one desk to stand next to the person who owns that desk. These two players must answer another card flashed to them. The loser sits down and the winner moves back one desk.

If two players answer the problem correctly and simultaneously, they are shown another problem until one player makes a mistake and must take his seat. The game moves up and down the aisles until each child has had a turn.

The final winner is known as the "cabbie" for the day. A bulletin board containing a paper taxi is constructed and the winner's name is put on the taxi to signify that he is the winner for the day.

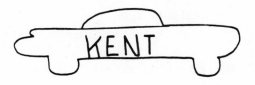

Jeopardy

Two teams are selected. The teacher reads the answer to both teams and they must supply the question. Points are awarded each time to the team with the first correct question.

Example

    Answer— Any symbol used to name a number.

    Question— What is a numeral?

    Answer— Any real number that can't be expressed as the quotient of two integers.

    Question— What is an irrational number?

    Answer— Any whole number greater than one whose only whole number factors are itself and one.

    Question— What is a prime number?

A Fraction Puzzle

Procedure: A girl kept every doll she had received since she was a baby. Later, however, she decided to get rid of most of them. She discarded ⅓ of the collection. Then she gave ⅔ of the remaining dolls to a little girl who lived nearby. The rest of the dolls, the very best ones, she kept. There were 12 of these. How many dolls did she have when she started?

Solution: Think of the dolls in three groups:

A—the total collection.

B—the dolls remaining after ⅓ of total was discarded.

C—the 12 dolls remaining after ⅔ of B had been given to the little girl.

Since 12 remained (group C) after ⅔ were given to the little girl, we know that 12 = ⅓. Therefore, ³⁄₃ = 36 (group B).

Now, 36 remained after ⅓ of group A was discarded, so 36 = ⅔ of group A. Therefore, 18 = ⅓, and ³⁄₃ (total of group A) = 54, the number of dolls in the original collection.

It's Your Move

Eight boys are going to run a relay race. There will be four boys on each team. The eight boys are wearing the numbers 1, 2, 3, 4, 5, 6, 7, and 8 on their shirts. The boys are standing in two groups. Those wearing the numbers 1, 2, 3, and 4 are in one group. Those wearing 5, 6, 7, and 8 are in the other group.

The coach notices that the sum of the numbers in the first group is ten, and that the sum of the numbers in the second group is 26.

"We can't have this," says the coach and moves the boys around to make the two new groups. The sum of the four numbers in each new group is the same.

Answer

8	7
5	6
3	4
2	1
18	18

Red Riding Hood and the Wolf

On a flannel board mount a house made of tagboard, placing the addition and subtraction facts to be used in each window and door. A wolf cutout is advanced one step toward the house each time an incorrect response is given as the leader points to a fact on a window or door. If the response is correct the shutters are closed, the contest being to see if all windows and doors can be closed before the wolf advances to the door.

Road Signs

Can you change these base 10 road signs to base 5 and base 3?

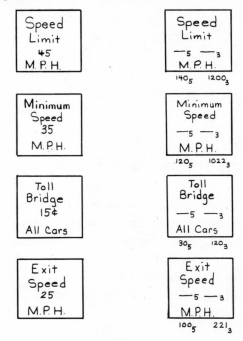

Base 3, April, 1968

The class can make calendars in a particular base, or in a different base for each month.

APRIL, 2200220						
SUN.	MON.	TUES.	WED.	THURS.	FRI.	SAT.
	1	2	10	11	12	20
21	22	100	101	102	110	111
112	120	121	122	200	201	202
210	211	212	220	221	222	1000
1001	1002	1010				

Base 6, May, 1968

At the beginning of each month, a calendar sheet is made by each child. It shows both the decimal system date and its equivalent date in another base.

1968, MAY, 13040						
SUN.	MON.	TUES.	WED.	THURS.	FRI.	SAT.
			1 1	2 2	3 3	4 4
5 5	6 10	7 11	8 12	9 13	10 14	11 15
12 20	13 21	14 22	15 23	16 24	17 25	18 30
19 31	20 32	21 33	22 34	23 35	24 40	25 41
26 42	27 43	28 44	29 45	30 50	31 51	

Multiplication Contest

East	West
4	8
7	3
2	4
5	6
3	5
8	7
6	2

chalkboard

1. Divide the pupils into an East team and a West team.
2. One representative from each team goes to the board.
3. The teacher says "six" and the two representatives write the products for six and each number listed.
4. The person who finished first with the correct products receives one tally for his team.

5. Two more pupils come to the board.

6. The teacher says "nine."

7. Continue the contest until one team receives a score of six.

Number Words

This is an activity to provide practice in Roman numerals and number words. The number of objects shown in Roman numerals is to be circled. Several other terms that may be used include: first, tenth, left, right, over, under, before, and after.

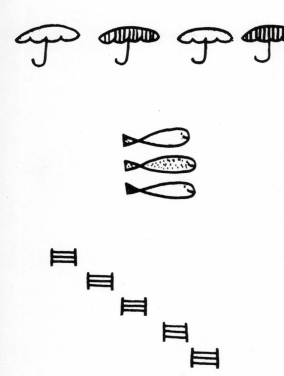

III   IV   V   VI

Which umbrellas have stripes? Circle the words.

first, second, last, third

II   IX   III   IV

Circle the fish *under* the spotted fish.

Put an X to the *left* of the *top* fish.

V   VII   X   VI

Circle the *middle* fence.

Put an X on the *fourth* fence.

Spin-a-Sentence Wheel

Construct this learning device and allow the pupils to recognize and understand relation symbols with it.

Example: 8 is greater than 4
            4 is less than 8

Fractions

Write the fractions to name the shaded parts:

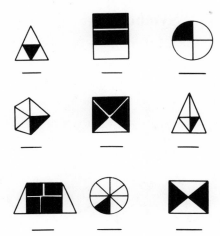

Mathematical Mobiles

Materials: Different colors of construction paper, tissue paper, cardboard, string or thread, strong wood sticks.

Procedure: Let us assume that the children have constructed mobiles in art so there will be no distraction from the math. From here, have each child choose a number and construct the processes and numbers that arrive at this numeral for an answer. Encourage each student to use different materials. Display mobiles by hanging them from the ceiling and go over the different numbers used.

Example: Has each child used all possibilities?

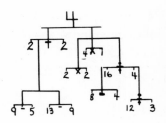

<u>Note</u>: Some numerals can be made larger than others.

Symbol Tree

Let the children make the symbols for trimming the tree. Each child identifies his symbol before hanging it on the tree. When the tree is filled, call on children to construct a number sentence using one or more of the symbols on the tree.

Peep Frame

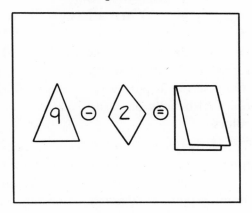

This is an easily constructed device for learning basic facts in all of the four operations.

In this example, the minuend and subtrahend are given. The child picks the correct number response and puts it under the flap to indicate a true mathematical statement.

Number Sentence Wheel Frames

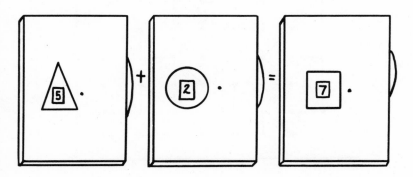

Cut three circular wheels with numbers 1 to 25 on them. Pin them to a piece of cardboard with an open geometric symbol cut out of it. The child or the teacher sets up the problem, and the child completes the statement by choosing the correct numeral on the third wheel.

Yarn Play

Materials: One pegboard 2 x 2 feet in area and a number of screws that will fit into every hole in the pegboard. (Only screw in part way so most of screw is left on top.) Also balls of yarn, usually from three to four colors.

Procedure: This activity can be set in the activity corner for extra time use. The object is to string different colors of yarn around each screw in a maze formation, trying to use as much yarn as possible. The only rule is that the different colors of yarn cannot touch or cross each other and every screw must be used.

5

Challenges in
Geometry

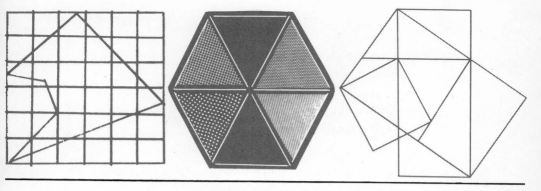

Arithme-Trick

Well, here's a bit which was new more than a thousand years ago when introduced by a Moroccan genius whose work was first called algebra. According to Mrs. Abdelkri Boujibar, director of the Museum of Morocco, this genius conceived the figures 0 through 9 which we know today as Arabic numerals, and he shaped them so that each contained an appropriate number of angles, as shown in the above illustration. His figure 1 contains one angle, his 2 contains two angles, his 3 contains three angles, etc. Zero, signifying nothing, had no angles.

Perception

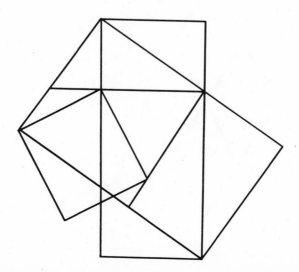

How many rectangles are in the picture?
How many triangles are in the picture?

Answer: 7 rectangles
              20 triangles

Arrangement Problem

Arrange the following so that they form four small diamonds or one large diamond by moving four lines only.

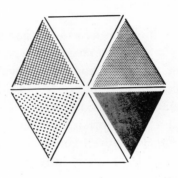

Answer

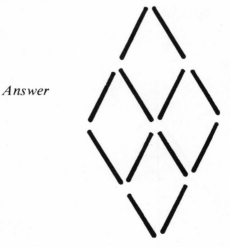

Estimating Areas

Students might draw irregular shapes on tissue or other transparent paper. Then, they can place these shapes over squared paper (such as graph paper) and count the squares enclosed by the shapes. After doing this, they can appreciate more fully the shortcut method we use for computing areas of rectangles and other parallelograms.

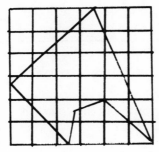

Picture Map

The lines on a map show us lines of latitude and longitude. The sets of lines form a system which makes it possible for us to locate any point on our maps.

What do you find located at the points listed below?

1. 40 north latitude, 115 west longitude.
2. 30 north latitude, 80 west longitude.
3. 45 north latitude, 85 west longitude.
4. 30 north latitude, 100 west longitude.
5. 25 north latitude, 115 west longitude.

Answers

1. A skier
2. A rocket
3. A tanker
4. An oil well
5. A sailfish

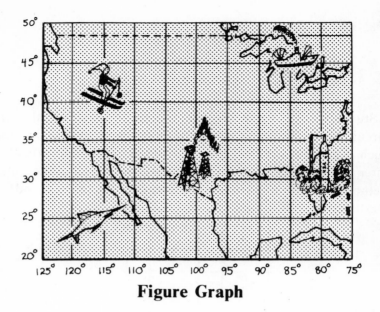

Figure Graph

Figure out the problem and mark it on the graph.

				Answers	
1.	$24 + 12 - 32 \div 2 =$	top	1.	2
	$42 \times 2 - 80 \div 4 =$	side		1
2.	$6 \times \frac{1}{2} - 2 =$	top	2.	1
	$30 \times \frac{1}{3} \div 5 =$	side		2
3.	$15 - 5 - 5 - 3 =$	top	3.	2
	$4 \times 6 + 3 \div 9 =$	side		3
4.	$7 \times 8 - 5 \div 17 =$	top	4.	3
	$2 + 10 \div 3 - 2 =$	side		2

Fill in the Missing Numbers

Fill in the missing numbers in the square.

Answers

1st row left to right 4, 9
2nd row left to right 9, 54
3rd row left to right 2, 9
4th row left to right 8, 64

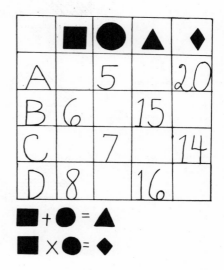

	■	●	▲	◆
A		5		20
B	6		15	
C		7		14
D	8		16	

■ + ● = ▲

■ × ● = ◆

Bingo

Geometry — Fractions — Time

This game will have three sets of cards. One set will contain fraction problems, pictures, or words of fractions. The second set will consist of geometric definitions or words. The third set will contain time problems, pictures, or words.

$\frac{1}{3}$ (A.M.)	$\frac{2}{8}$ one	$\frac{9}{27}$ 2:00	$\frac{1}{6}$ Ten
$\frac{4}{12}$ 6:00	$\frac{3}{7}$ 12:00	$\frac{2}{5}$ (P.M.)	$\frac{3}{18}$ 2:15
$\frac{6}{16}$ 12:00	$\frac{2}{9}$ 4:00	$\frac{1}{3}$ o'clock	$\frac{1}{2}$ 3:30
$\frac{1}{4}$ 8:30	$\frac{2}{8}$ 1:00	$\frac{1}{10}$ 6:30	$\frac{7}{16}$ 6:30

Match the Formula with the Polygon

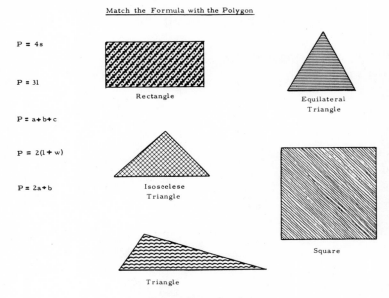

P = 4s

P = 3l

P = a+b+c

P = 2(l + w)

P = 2a+b

Rectangle

Equilateral
Triangle

Isoscelese
Triangle

Square

Triangle

Mr. Symbol

Draw a man using the following symbols:

   A *circle* for his head.

   A *union* symbol for his mouth.

   2 *difference* symbols for his eyes.

   An *intersection* symbol for his nose.

   A *long rectangle* for his neck.

   A *circle* for his body.

   2 *straight lines* for his arms and legs.

   2 *squares* for hands.

   2 *rectangles* for feet.

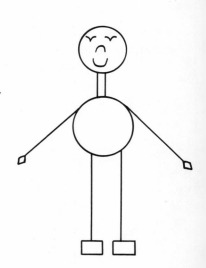

Fractions

Shade the correct part of each region. Circle the correct dot on each number line.

⅓ of ½ =

⅓ × ½ =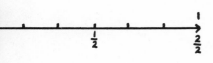

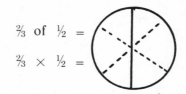

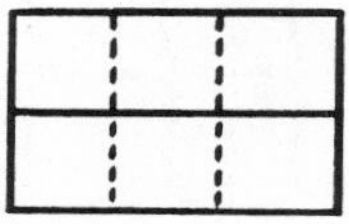

½ of ¼ =

½ × ¼ =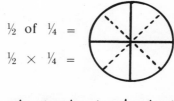

⅓ of ⅓ =

⅓ × ⅓ =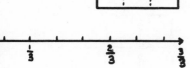

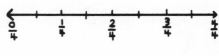

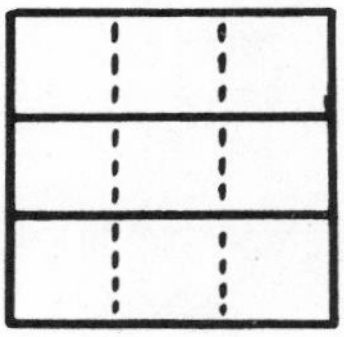

⅔ of ½ =

⅔ × ½ =

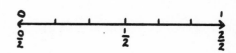

Try these:

1. ⅓ × ¼ =   4. ⅕ × ⅑ =

2. ¼ × ⅐ =   5. ⅑ × ½ =

3. ⅓ × ¹⁄₁₆ =   6. ⅓ × ⅙ =

Matchsticks Placement

Procedure: By removing five of the matchsticks, leave three
squares.

Solution

Procedure: By removing six of the matchsticks, leave two squares.

Solution

Matchsticks on the Square

Procedure: Can you change nine squares to only two squares by
removing eight matchsticks ?

Solution

Matchsticks into Five

Procedure: By moving three of these ten matchsticks to another position can you change them into a five?

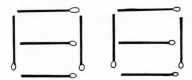

Solution

Matchsticks into Ten

Procedure: By adding five more matchsticks change them into a
ten.

Solution

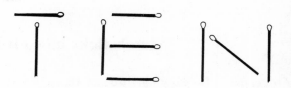

Matchsticks into Nine

Procedure: By adding five more matchsticks change them into a
nine.

Solution

Matchsticks on the Square

Procedure   By removing four matchsticks only five squares will remain. What four sticks are to be removed?

Solution

More Toothpick Teasers

1. The three squares are made with ten toothpicks. Can you take away two toothpicks and leave just two squares of the same size?

2. These four equal squares are made with 13 toothpicks. Take away one toothpick and leave three equal squares.

3. The four equal squares are made with 12 toothpicks. Can you take away two toothpicks and leave only two squares? (The squares left need not be of equal size.)

4. Again four equal squares are made with 12 toothpicks. Now the problem is to move (do not take away) three toothpicks so as to form three equal squares.

Answers

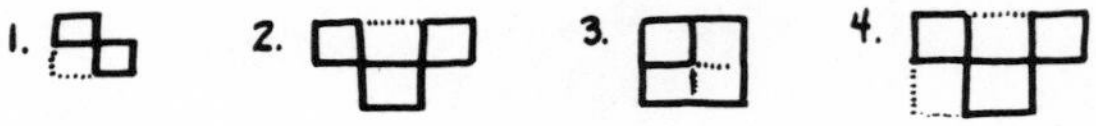

5. Make three equal squares with 12 toothpicks as shown below. Now take away one toothpick and leave the word "one."

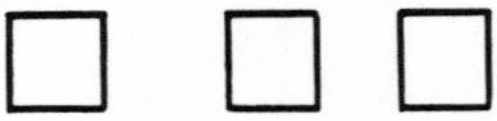

6. Here we have nine equal squares made with 24 toothpicks. Can you take away four toothpicks and leave just five equal squares?

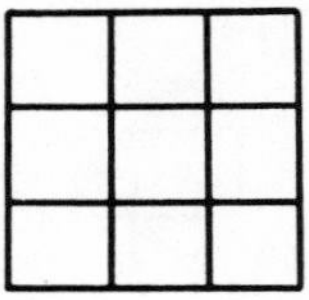

Answers

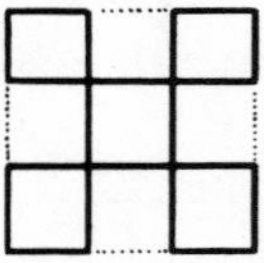

Fill in the Missing Numbers

	▲	☆	▦	●
A	10		6	
B	8			9
C		5		11
D	3			5
E		4		11
F	9		9	

▲ + ☆ = ●

▲ − ☆ = ▦

Answers:
A=4, 14   D=2, 1
B=1, 7   E=7, 3
C=6, 1   F=0, 9

Fill in the Missing Fractions

	●	▲	⬬	☆
A	1/4		0	
B	3/8			5/8
C		1/3		1
D	5/8			7/8
E		1/3		5/6
F	1/10		0	

● + ▲ = ☆

● − ▲ = ⬟

Answers:
A=1/4, 1/4, 0, 1/2
B=3/8, 1/4, 1/8, 5/8
C=2/3, 1/3, 1/3, 1
D=5/8, 1/4, 3/8, 7/8
E=1/2, 1/3, 1/6, 5/6
F−1/10, 2/5, 0, 1/2

6

Magic Figures

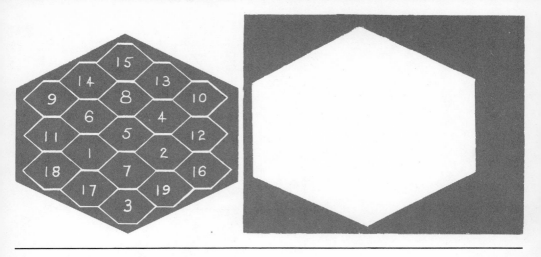

Magic Square

$\frac{1}{8}$		$\frac{1}{4}$	$\frac{3}{8}$
	$\frac{3}{8}$	$\frac{1}{8}$	
	O	$\frac{7}{8}$	$\frac{1}{2}$
$\frac{7}{8}$			O

Answers

1st row $\frac{5}{8}$

2nd row $\frac{3}{8}$, $\frac{1}{2}$

3rd row 0

4th row $\frac{3}{8}$, $\frac{1}{8}$

The answer must equal $1\frac{3}{8}$

Magic Square

Complete the following square so horizontally the sums are equal and vertically the sums are equal.

125

1⅓	2½	⅙
	1½	2⅙
1⅚		1⅔
2⅓		
	1⅙	2

Answer

⅓   Horizontally the answer must equal 4.
½

1, ⅔   Vertically the answer must equal 6⅔
⅚

Magic Square

Complete the following magic square so that each row adds equally in all directions.

⅙	2		2⅓
	2⅙		1⅚
1⅔		2⅔	
2½		1½	⅔

Answer

1⅙
1⅓,   ⅓   The answer must equal 5⅔
½,   ⅚
1

126

Mixed Numbers Puzzles

Purpose: As enrichment for those who need no additional practice in the addition of mixed numbers.

Procedure: The principle is the same as that of the more common magic squares used with whole numbers; that is, the sums of the rows, columns, and diagonals must all add up to the same numeral.

(Diagonals, rows, and columns add up to $10\frac{1}{2}$)

Magic Square 1

3	$5\frac{1}{2}$	2
$2\frac{1}{2}$	$3\frac{1}{2}$	$4\frac{1}{2}$
5	$1\frac{1}{2}$	4

(Diagonals, rows, and columns add up to $9\frac{3}{4}$)

Magic Square 2

$2\frac{3}{4}$	$5\frac{1}{4}$	$1\frac{3}{4}$
$2\frac{1}{4}$	$3\frac{1}{4}$	$4\frac{1}{4}$
$4\frac{3}{4}$	$1\frac{1}{4}$	$3\frac{3}{4}$

(Diagonals, rows, and columns add up to $9\frac{3}{8}$)

Magic Square 3

$2\frac{5}{8}$	$5\frac{1}{8}$	$1\frac{5}{8}$
$2\frac{1}{8}$	$3\frac{1}{8}$	$4\frac{1}{8}$
$4\frac{5}{8}$	$1\frac{1}{8}$	$3\frac{5}{8}$

Like and Unlike Fractions Puzzles

Purpose: As an enrichment for those who need no additional practice in the addition of like and unlike fractions.

Procedure: The principle is the same as that of the more common magic squares used with whole numbers; that is, the sum of the rows, columns, and diagonals must all add up to the same numeral.

(Diagonals, rows, and columns add up to $^{15}\!/_{10}$'s or $1\frac{1}{2}$)

Magic Square 1

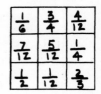

$\frac{4}{10}$	$\frac{3}{10}$	$\frac{8}{10}$
$\frac{9}{10}$	$\frac{5}{10}$	$\frac{1}{10}$
$\frac{2}{10}$	$\frac{7}{10}$	$\frac{6}{10}$

(Diagonals, rows, and columns add up to $^{15}\!/_{12}$'s or $1\frac{1}{4}$)

Magic Square 2

$\frac{1}{6}$	$\frac{3}{4}$	$\frac{4}{12}$
$\frac{7}{12}$	$\frac{5}{12}$	$\frac{1}{4}$
$\frac{1}{2}$	$\frac{1}{12}$	$\frac{2}{3}$

(Diagonals, rows, and columns add up to $^{24}\!/_{16}$'s or $1\frac{1}{2}$)

Magic Square 3

$\frac{9}{16}$	$\frac{5}{8}$	$\frac{5}{16}$
$\frac{1}{4}$	$\frac{8}{16}$	$\frac{3}{4}$
$\frac{11}{16}$	$\frac{3}{8}$	$\frac{7}{16}$

Magic Squares

2	9	4
7	5	3
6	1	8

15

16	2	3	13
5	11	10	8
9	7	6	12
4	14	15	1

34

19	16	13	28
14	27	20	15
26	11	18	21
17	22	25	12

$\frac{1}{5}$	$\frac{9}{10}$	$\frac{2}{5}$
$\frac{7}{10}$	$\frac{1}{2}$	$\frac{3}{10}$
$\frac{3}{5}$	$\frac{1}{10}$	$\frac{4}{5}$

$1\frac{1}{2}$

Find the correct numbers that will cause columns, horizontal lines, and diagonal rows of figures to add up to the same total amount, in each figure. Each square has its own total amount, as indicated by the typewritten number next to each square.

Magic Squares

The sum of the fractional numerals in each row, each column, and each diagonal must be the same.

$\frac{6}{8}$		$\frac{4}{4}$
$\frac{14}{16}$	$\frac{10}{16}$	
	$\frac{9}{2}$	$\frac{2}{4}$

Answers

Row 1 — $\frac{2}{16}$ or equivalent

Row 2 — $\frac{12}{32}$ or equivalent

Row 3 — $\frac{2}{8}$ or equivalent

The answer must equal $1\frac{7}{8}$.

Practice in Multiplying Mentally

Purpose: To give practice in multiplying "mentally" by small multipliers as an aid to the multiplication children encounter in division examples.

Procedure:

1. Have the children copy this magic square from the board. Tell them to prove that it is a magic square.

1	6	7	2	9
2	9	1	6	7
6	7	2	9	1
9	1	6	7	2
7	2	9	1	6

2. Have the children multiply each number in the above magic square by 4.

4	24	28	8	36
8	36	4	24	28
24	28	8	36	4
36	4	24	28	8
28	8	36	4	24

3. Have the children subtract 4 from each number in the above magic square.

0	20	24	4	32
4	32	0	20	24
20	24	4	32	0
32	0	20	24	4
24	4	32	0	20

4. Have the children divide each number in the second magic square above by 2.

2	12	14	4	18
4	18	2	12	14
12	14	4	18	2
18	2	12	14	4
14	4	18	2	12

Magic Squares

The square below contains all the numbers from 1 to 16. Is it a magic square? What is the sum of the numbers in each row? What is the sum of the numbers in each column? What is the sum of the numbers on each arrow?

This is more magic than most squares! What is the sum of the numbers in each corner? What is the sum of the numbers in the four corner squares? There are still other ways of getting the sum 34. How many can you find?

4	9	5	16
14	7	11	2
15	6	10	3
1	12	8	13

Are these magic squares?

15	16	22	3	9
8	14	20	21	2
1	7	13	19	25
24	5	6	12	18
17	23	4	10	11

XIII	III	II	XVI
VIII	X	XI	V
XII	VI	VII	IX
I	XV	XIV	IV

The answer must equal 34.

The answer must equal 65.

Reducing Box

By reducing all the fractions in the nine boxes you should be able to add the fractions in any direction to total 1½.

$\frac{4}{8}$	$\frac{3}{6}$	$\frac{10}{20}$
$\frac{5}{10}$	$\frac{9}{18}$	$\frac{14}{28}$
$\frac{7}{14}$	$\frac{8}{16}$	$\frac{30}{60}$

Magic Square

17	24	1	8	15
23	5	7	14	16
4	6	13	20	22
10	12	19	21	3
11	18	25	2	9

Find the correct numbers that will cause each column and each horizontal row and diagonal row of figures to add to the same total (65). There are 25 squares in this figure and the numbers used will be 1 through 25. Good Luck!

Magic Square

Complete the following magic squares so that each row adds equally in all directions. Can you find the similarity between these two magic squares?

23	1	
5	17	
	13	15

Answers
7
9

They should all total 31.

Answer
3

Answer
Divide the answer for the first magic square by 2 and you get the answer for the second magic square.

$11\frac{1}{2}$	$\frac{1}{2}$	
$2\frac{1}{2}$	$8\frac{1}{2}$	
	$6\frac{1}{2}$	$7\frac{1}{2}$

Answers
$3\frac{1}{2}$
$4\frac{1}{2}$
They should all total $15\frac{1}{2}$.

Answer
$1\frac{1}{2}$

Magic "Base" Square

Fill in the blank squares so that the sums equal 66_8. The total added together equals 54.

	11_5	
	30_6	
33_4		100_3

Answer
Convert all numbers to the base 10
then solve problem.

27	6	21
12	18	24
15	30	9

Base Magic Squares

Directions: Complete the following magic squares so that each row adds equally in all directions and change the base numbers given to all base 10 numbers.

121_3	10_2		23_5
12_3		1010_2	
	12_5		14_8
100_2		13_{12}	1_3

Completed Solution

134

16	2	3	13
5	11	10	8
9	7	6	12
4	14	15	1

The answer must equal 34.

Magic Square with Fractions

All squares added together must total two.

	1/2	1/4	
2/8	7/8	3/4	1/8
		1/2	
1/4			3/4

Answers:
3/4, 1/2, 1/4, 1/2
2/8, 7/8, 3/4, 1/8
3/4, 1/8, 1/2, 5/8
1/4, 1/2, 1/2, 3/4

Magic Square

The total must equal 20.

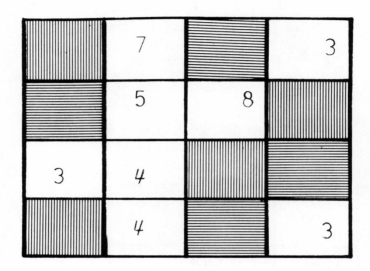

Answer:

8 7 2 3
5 5 8 2
3 4 1 12
4 4 9 3

Magic Square

Procedure: The sum of the numbers in each column, each row, and each diagonal should be 34.

1	11	6	16
8	14	3	9
15	5	12	2
10	4	13	7

Magic Square

Procedure: The sum of the numbers in each column and each row should be ⁵⁄₂.

⅙	⅓	½	⅔	⅚
⅓	½	⅔	⅚	⅙
½	⅔	⅚	⅙	⅓
⅔	⅚	⅙	⅓	½
⅚	⅙	⅓	½	⅔

Magic Square

Procedure: The sum of the numbers in each column, each row, and each diagonal should be 3.4.

0.7	1.3	0.4	1.0
0.2	1.2	0.5	1.5
0.9	0.3	1.4	0.8
1.6	0.6	1.1	0.1

Magic Triangle

Arrange the numerals 1 to 6 in the pentagon so that the sum of three numbers along each side is 12. Now try it so the sum is two by using fractions.

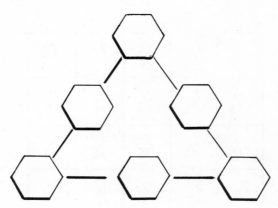

Answer

```
    4              2/3
  2   3          1/3   1/2
6   1   5      1   1/6   5/6
```

Magic Hexagon

The sum of the numbers in each column, each row, and each diagonal should be 38.

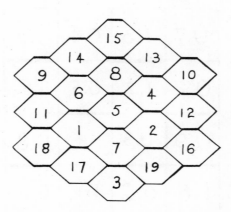

Fractional Magic Squares

Directions: Complete the following magic squares so that each row adds equally in all directions using the following fractions—½, ²⁄₄, ³⁄₆, ⁹⁄₁₈. The answer must equal 1⅚.

$\frac{3}{6}$	$\frac{1}{2}$	$\frac{2}{4}$	$\frac{9}{18}$
$\frac{2}{4}$	$\frac{9}{18}$	$\frac{3}{6}$	$\frac{1}{2}$
$\frac{9}{18}$	$\frac{2}{4}$	$\frac{1}{2}$	$\frac{3}{6}$
$\frac{1}{2}$	$\frac{3}{6}$	$\frac{9}{18}$	$\frac{2}{4}$

Roman Magic Squares

Directions: Complete the following magic squares so that each row adds equally in all directions using Roman numerals. The answer must equal 15.

II	IX	IV
VII	V	III
VI	I	VIII

7

Discovering
Number
Patterns

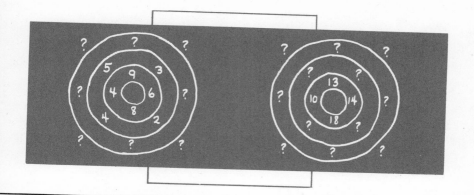

Number Patterns

The number 1,234 or one thousand, two hundred and thirty-four can be expressed as four units, three tens, two hundreds, and one thousand. We could draw a picture that looks like this:

```
x x x x   units
  x x x   tens
    x x   hundreds
      x   thousand
```

Can you draw pictures like the above for these numbers?

54,321

```
    x
  x x
x x x
x x x x
x x x x x
```

12,321

```
    x
  x x
x x x
  x x
    x
```

5,116,531

```
      x
    x x x
  x x x x x
x x x x x x
      x
      x
  x x x x x
```

3,212,321

```
    x
  x x
x x x
  x x
    x
  x x
x x x
```

7,654,567

```
x x x x x x x
x x x x x x
x x x x x
  x x x x
x x x x x
x x x x x x
x x x x x x x
```

1,357,531

```
      x
    x x x
  x x x x x
x x x x x x x
  x x x x x
    x x x
      x
```

Perfect Numbers

Perfect numbers are rare, and while their factors add up to the number, the product of the factor does not. This is true only for 4 and 6. Look at these numbers:

$6 = 1 + 2 + 3$ $496 =$

$28 = 1 + 2 + 4 + 7 + 14$ $8,128 =$

Can you break these two remaining numbers down to their proper factors? It will be a long answer.

Number Sequence and Order

Write this number on your paper:

037037037037	×	3	=	111111111111	×	18	=
037037037037	×	6	=	222222222222	×	21	=
037037037037	×	9	=	333333333333	×	24	=
	×	12	=		×	28	=
	×	15	=		×	30	=

What do you think the rest of the numbers will be like?

Can you complete the pattern in this example?

$$1 \times 8 + 1 = 9$$
$$12 \times 8 + 2 = 98$$
$$123 \times 8 + 3 = 987$$

Now figure out the rest:

$1,234 \times 8 + 4 = $ _____ $1,234,567 \times 8 + 7 = $ _____

$12,345 \times 8 + 5 = $ _____ $12,345,678 \times 8 + 8 = $ _____

$123,456 \times 8 + 6 = $ _____ $123,456,789 \times 8 + 9 = $ _____

Number Pattern Puzzle

Can you double the numerals from 1 to 20 to find the way to connect these dots and make a picture?

Number Pattern Puzzle

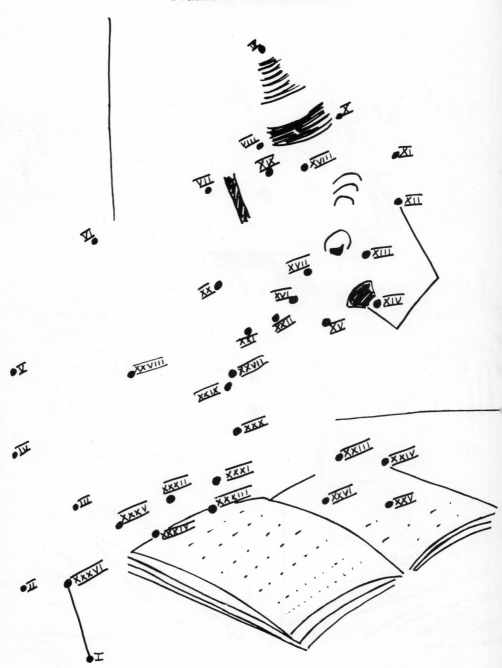

Number Patterns for Squares

You can establish a number pattern for any squared number. Look at the following examples:

$1^2 = 1 = 1$ $= 1$

$2^2 = 4 = 1 + 2 + 1$ $= 4$

$3^2 = 9 = 1 + 2 + 3 + 2 + 1$ $= 9$

$4^2 = 16 = 1 + 2 + 3 + 4 + 3 + 2 + 1$ $= 16$

Now complete the following:

$5^2 =$ $=$

$6^2 =$ $=$

$7^2 =$ $=$

$8^2 =$ $=$

Did you understand the procedure?
Here is what the 9^2 looks like:

$9^2 = 81 = 1 + 2 + 3 + 4 + 5 + 6 + 7 + 8 + 9 + 8 +$
$7 + 6 + 5 + 4 + 3 + 2 + 1$ $= 81$

Division Patterns

Copy the numbers in Column A. Divide each of these numbers by 9 and place in Column B. Do you see the pattern in each of the columns?

Column A		Column B
81	divide by 9	9
882	divide by 9	98
8,883	divide by 9	987

Now do the rest.

88,884	divide by 9	_____
888,885	divide by 9	_____
8,888,886	divide by 9	_____
88,888,887	divide by 9	_____
888,888,888	divide by 9	_____
8,888,888,889	divide by 9	_____

Another Division Pattern

Copy the following examples and then write the answer beside each example:

$$11 - 2 \div 9 = 1$$
$$111 - 3 \div 9 = 12$$
$$1,111 - 4 \div 9 = 123$$

(now do the rest)

$$11,111 - 5 \div 9 =$$
$$111,111 - 6 \div 9 =$$
$$1,111,111 - 7 \div 9 =$$
$$11,111,111 - 8 \div 9 =$$
$$111,111,111 - 9 \div 9 =$$
$$1,111,111,111 - 10 \div 9 =$$

Multiplication Pattern

Look at the following example and then multiply:

$$37 \times 3 \quad = \quad 111$$
$$37 \times 6 \quad = \quad 222$$
$$37 \times 9 \quad = \quad ?$$
$$37 \times 12 \quad = \quad ?$$
$$37 \times 15 \quad = \quad ?$$
$$37 \times 18 \quad = \quad ?$$
$$37 \times 21 \quad = \quad ?$$
$$37 \times 24 \quad = \quad ?$$
$$37 \times 27 \quad = \quad ?$$

Can you explain why the pattern forms?

Cyclic Numbers

Look at these six numbers:

031,746   174,603   317,460   460,317

603,174   746,031

These are called cyclic (or circular) numbers. Do you see why they are so named?

Each of them is formed from the same figures:

0, 3, 1, 7, 4, and 6

Arrange these figures around a circle. Then look at them again. To make cyclic numbers, you begin with a different numeral each time, but you keep the same order. The direction is always clockwise:

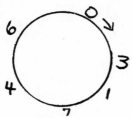

Subtract each smaller number from the next larger number:

174,603	317,460	460,317	603,174	746,031
−031,746	−174,603	−317,460	−460,317	−603,174

The answer is: 142,857 each time.

. . . .

Divide 999,999 by 7.

Multiply the answer by 1, then by 2, then by 3, by 4, then by 5, and lastly, by 6.

Are the answers cyclic numbers?

Now multiply 142,857 by 7 and "break the charm."

Round and Round

Choose any four numbers, such as 5, 8, 7, 3. Arrange them in any order around a circle. Now subtract each number from any larger number next to it. Place these answers on a bigger circle. Put each answer between the two numbers subtracted.

Do the same thing with the four numbers on the second circle that you did with the first four numbers. Place the answers on a still bigger circle.

If you continue this long enough, a point is reached where the four numbers are equal.

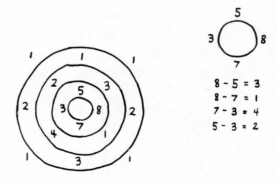

Now try it with these numbers:

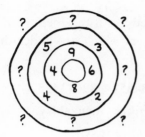 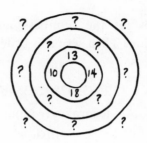

Fibonacci Sequence

Look at the following numbers:

1, 1, 2, 3, 5,__,__,__,__,__

Do you recognize a sequence?

Answer: Add the terms immediately preceding the term you
are trying to determine.

Ex. $1 + 1 = 2$ $1 + 2 = 3$ $2 + 3 = 5$

Palindrome

A *palindrome* is a word, sentence, or verse that is spelled the
same from right to left as from left to right.

The Greek word "palindromos" means "running back again."
Names like *Eve, Otto, Ada* and words like *gag, noon,* and *radar* are
palindromes.

Can you create some palindromes using numerals?

Example: 1 2 3 4 3 2 1

6 3 6

57675

There are infinite possibilities.

Odd and Even Numbers

Look at the numbers and the letters listed below in each grouping. Then write in order the letters which are under the odd numbers.

1268354789263546789   2234857   896432257

feeqraxcytwkiolmnps   ppajkre   qeuzahisy

Answer: Fractions are easy

Number Pattern Puzzle

Connect the dots and see who is with us today!

Number Pattern Puzzle

Connect the dots (base five).

Number Pattern Puzzle

Connect the numbers from one to fifty-two and find out what is looking at you.

Number Pattern Puzzle

Connect the numbered dots with straight lines. What animal have you drawn?

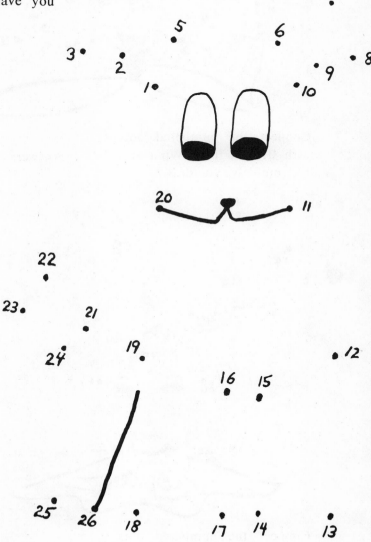

Answer: a dog

Connect the numbered dots with straight lines. What animal have you drawn?

Answer: a cat

Connect the numbered dots with straight lines. What have you drawn?

Answer: a clown

Surprise Dots

Connect the numbered dots. What animal is it?

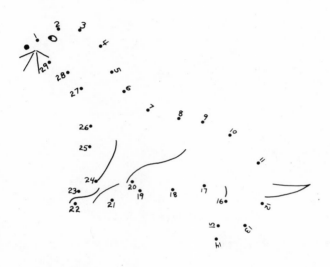

Answer
Seal

Who Am I?

Connect the dots by adding the numbers next to each dot.

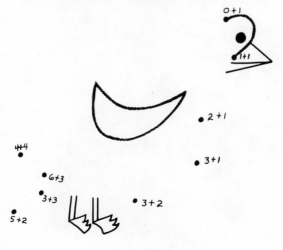

Guess Who

Objective: Connect the dots by counting by fives and see who your favorite friend is.

Picture Pattern Puzzle

Connect the following dots in the order in which they appear.

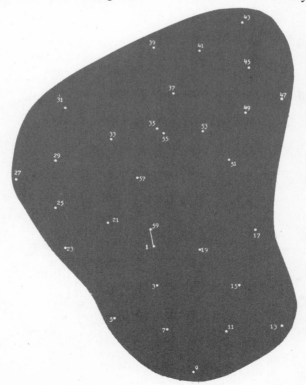

Charley Connect

The dots are to be connected following what type of sequence? (5, 10, 15, 20, etc.) Can you renumber the dots using a sequence of 3? (3, 6, 9, 12, etc.)

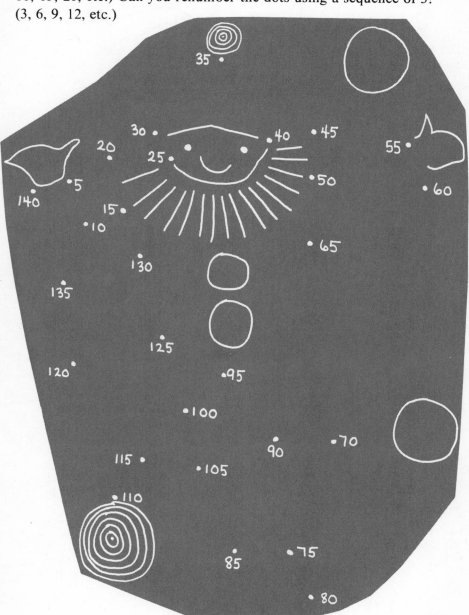

Santa

$2 + 4 =$
$7 - 5 =$
$4 \times 5 =$
$3 \times 3 =$
$6 + 6 =$
$15 - 7 =$
$3 + 8 =$
$12 \div 4 =$
$7 \times 2 =$
$15 \div 3 =$
$21 - 4 =$
$11 + 8 =$
$7 - 6 =$
$4 \times 4 =$
$8 \div 2 =$
$20 - 7 =$
$5 + 5 =$
$14 \div 2 =$
$6 \times 3 =$
$20 - 5 =$

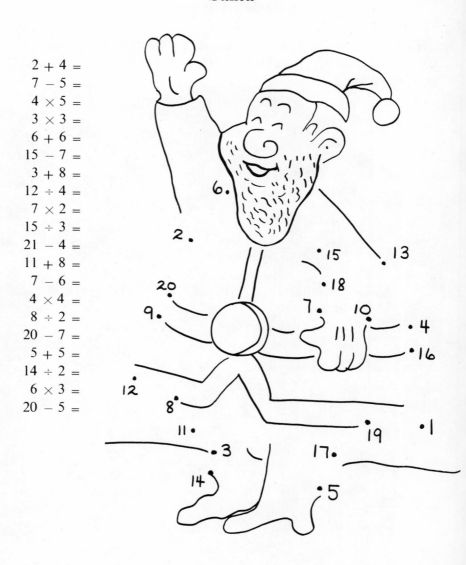

First do the examples. Then connect the like
numbered dots to complete the picture in the
same order as your answers.

Color Each Number

Add the numbers and then cover each number with a certain color. Notice the pattern.

+	0	1	2	3	4	5	6	7	8	9
0	0	1	2	3	4	5	6	7	8	9
1	1	2	3	4	5	6	7	8	9	10
2	2	3	4	5	6	7	8	9	10	11
3	3	4	5	6	7	8	9	10	11	12
4	4	5	6	7	8	9	10	11	12	13
5	5	6	7	8	9	10	11	12	13	14
6	6	7	8	9	10	11	12	13	14	15
7	7	8	9	10	11	12	13	14	15	16
8	8	9	10	11	12	13	14	15	16	17
9	9	10	11	12	13	14	15	16	17	18

Dot-to-Dot in Bases

Give children mimeographed sheets of a dot-to-dot progression of different bases. The example below is done in base 8 and the figure implied is obvious.

Variations: Different bases could be in one entire picture. Children could make up their own dot-to-dots.

8

Picture
Number
Puzzles

Zelda Zebra

Solve each problem correctly. If the answer is 2, color red.

answer is 4 - blue
answer is 6 - green
answer is 8 - yellow
answer is 10 - brown

Missing Circle

The design below was made by a Spirograph from Kenner. The object is to discover what missing number will equal ten.

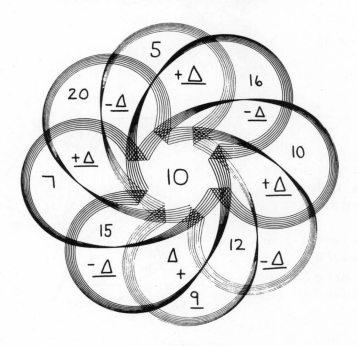

Time Dividing

Procedure: Have the student draw the face of a clock on paper. Ask the student to divide the clock into three parts with two straight lines so that the sum of the numbers in the three parts are equal.

Solution:

Walter Weight

Various combinations of numerals may be labeled on one side of the weights. What poundage is needed on the opposite side to balance the weights?

The child thinking of the most weight combinations wins. Examples for this problem shown include: 30 10 10, 40 5 5. Color Walter Weight.

Bulletin Board

How many "SCENTS" can you find!

Submarine

Materials: Spinner numbered from 1 to 3

Small bowl labeled "Ocean" containing math problems

2 felt frogmen

Flannel board

20 numbered squares of felt

Felt submarine and one ball of colored yarn

Directions: One player spins and whatever number it stops on is the number of squares of rope the child moves his frogman down. A question is then chosen from the bowl labeled "Ocean." If answered correctly his frogman remains where he is. If answered incorrectly he must move his frogman *up* the rope the number of squares shown on the spinner. The first of the two players to reach the submarine is the winner and captain of the ship. The winner's name is printed on the submarine signifying he is the new captain.

Picture Number Puzzle

If answer is 2, color the block yellow.

If answer is 3, color the block orange.

If answer is 4, color the block red.

If answer is 5, color the block blue.

If answer is 6, color the block green.

If answer is 7, color the block violet.

Picture Number Puzzle

Fill in the missing number. All answers should equal eight. Then color the turkey.

Multiplication Flower

Procedure:

1. Complete the flower by multiplying petals by the center number.

   Try different center numbers.

2. Place colors over the numbers and set up a key.

   Example: blue - 1

   red - 2

   Work with a partner to do multiplication by colors instead of numbers.

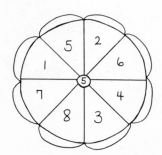

Hopper

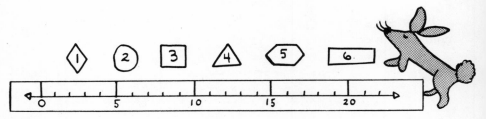

Each shape shows a numeral. Match the shapes of the frames below with the shapes above. Write Hopper's trips with the numerals in the frames. Find where Hopper goes on each trip.

Trip 1 = 12 – ② – △ – ③ = ▽

Trip 2 = 13 – □ – ○ – □ – ○ = ▽

Trip 3 = 10 – ○ – ⬡ – ◇ – ◇ = ▽

Trip 4 = 12 – ○ – ○ – ▭ = ▽

Trip 5 = 13 – ⬡ – □ – ○ = ▽

Trip 6 = 11 – △ – ◇ – ○ = ▽

Picture Number Puzzle

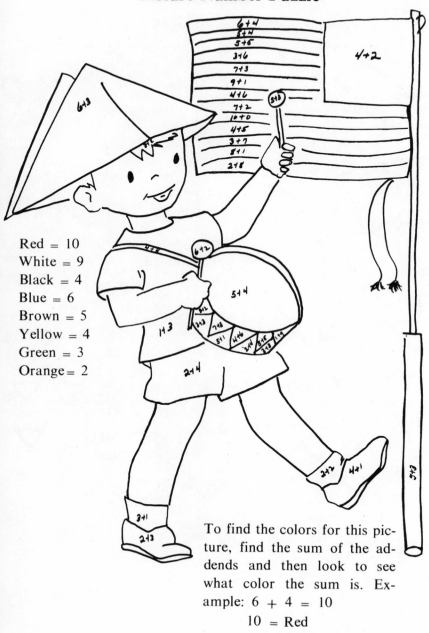

Red = 10
White = 9
Black = 4
Blue = 6
Brown = 5
Yellow = 4
Green = 3
Orange = 2

To find the colors for this picture, find the sum of the addends and then look to see what color the sum is. Example: 6 + 4 = 10
  10 = Red

Picture Number Puzzle

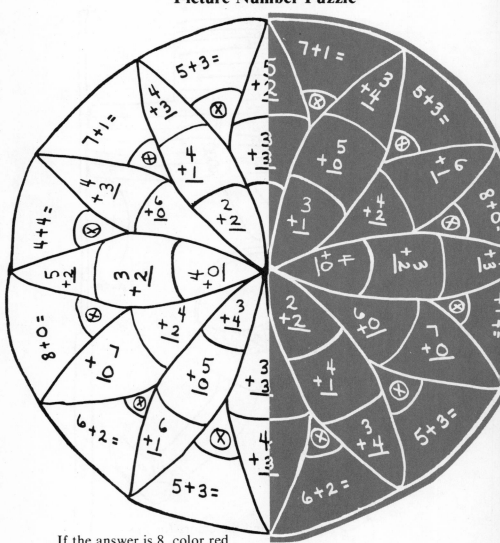

If the answer is 8, color red

7, orange

6, brown

5, blue

4, green

x, yellow

Picture Number Puzzle

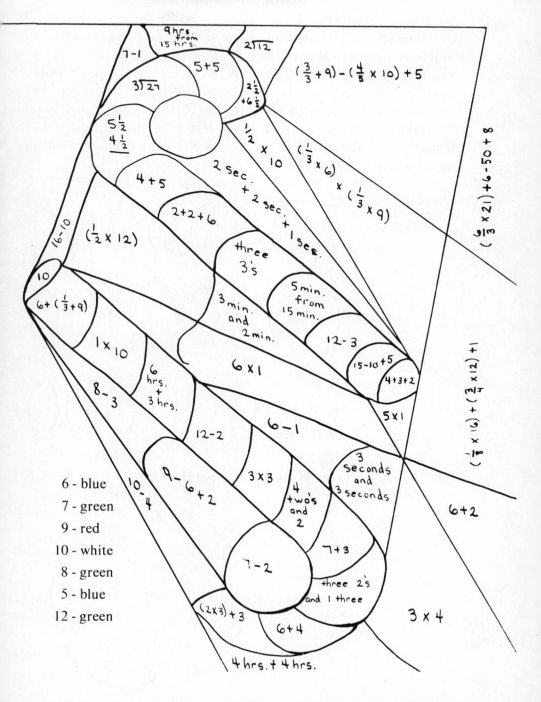

9 hrs. from 15 hrs.

2√12

7−1

5+5

3√27

2½ +6½

$(\frac{3}{3}+9)-(\frac{4}{5}\times 10)+5$

5½
4½

½ × 10

$(\frac{1}{3}\times 6)\times(\frac{1}{3}\times 9)$

$(\frac{6}{3}\times 21)+6-50+8$

4+5

2 sec. + 2 sec. + 1 sec.

16−10

$(\frac{1}{2}\times 12)$

2+2+6

10

three 3's

3 min. and 2 min.

5 min. from 15 min.

$6+(\frac{1}{3}+9)$

1 × 10

6 hrs. + 3 hrs.

6 × 1

12−3

15−10+5
4+3+2

$(\frac{1}{8}\times 16)+(\frac{3}{4}\times 12)+1$

8−3

12−2

6−1

5 × 1

10−4

9−6+2

3 × 3

4 two's and 2

3 seconds and 3 seconds

6 - blue
7 - green
9 - red
10 - white
8 - green
5 - blue
12 - green

7−2

7+3

three 2's and 1 three

6+2

(2×3)+3

6+4

3 × 4

4 hrs. + 4 hrs.

Fishing for Time

Make up cards in the form of fish with the face of a clock and a different time on each. (Colors of clock correspond to colors on pupil's paper clock.) Turn all cards face down and have each child pick or "catch" a fish. When he catches a fish, he must call out the correct time. If the answer is correct, the child keeps the fish; if not, he turns the fish face down again and mixes it among the fish to be caught. After all the fish are caught, the child with the biggest catch is the winner.

Example

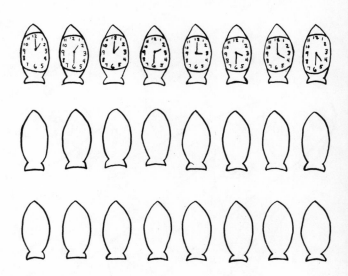

Roman Numerals

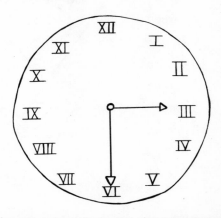

Move the hands on the clock:

1. What two numbers on the clock make   8
2. What two numbers on the clock make   3
3. What two numbers on the clock make   7
4. What two numbers on the clock make   9

Picture Number Puzzle

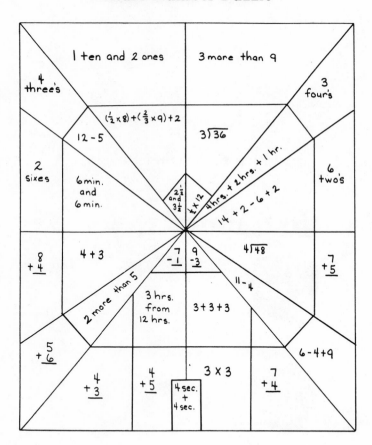

6 - purple   8 - black   11 - green

7 - brown   9 - yellow   12 - blue

Oliver the Octopus

Find the missing number to make the sum of 18.

Picture Number Puzzle

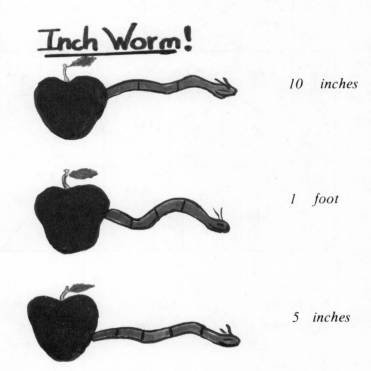

10   inches

1   foot

5   inches

Each segment of the worm represents one inch. Below the worm is given its entire length. How many inches are left inside the apple? Write your answer on the apple.

Picture Number Puzzle

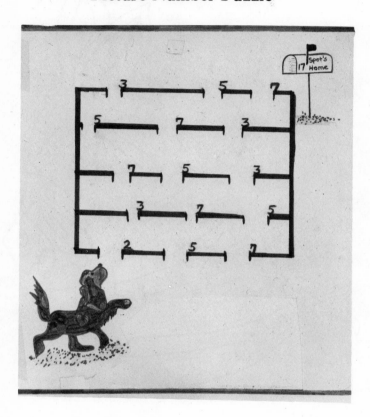

Help Spot find his way home. He may enter wherever there is an opening and continue to the mailbox. Each opening has a number which you must add to your score as you pass through. The object is to make the total of exactly *seventeen.*

(*Answer* — 5, 3, 3, 3, 3)

Color Quiz

Work the problems within this figure. If your answer is other than ten, leave it alone. If your answer is ten, color it black.

Picture Number Puzzle

Make your own code name by computation with the digits of a telephone. Find the numbers that correspond with the letters of your name, add them up!

For example:

Margaret is equivalent to 62742738. Her "code name" then is 39. What's yours?

Picture Number Puzzle

The cat in this diagram is made up entirely of figures. Try to find them, add them up. Your total should be 128. See how close you can come!

Picture Number Puzzle

1. Find all the factors of *12* and put them in the *clown's right hand.*

2. Find all of the factors of *16* and write them in the balloons in the *clown's left hand.*

3. Add up all of your balloons.

Picture Number Puzzle

This house is made up of nine geometrical figures. Can you find them?

Answer

1 circle	1 parallelogram
2 squares	1 triangle
2 trapezoids	2 rectangles

Picture Number Puzzle

This deer has a number in his ear and some numbers on the Christmas balls located on his antlers. Add up the numbers on the balls and fill in the number that should be in the empty ball if all the balls equal the same number that is in the deer's ear.

9

Puzzlers

Recognizing Odd Numbers

COLOR ALL THREE'S BLUE
COLOR ALL SEVEN'S RED
COLOR ALL FIVE'S GREEN
COLOR ALL NINE'S BLACK

All the Numbers Equal 24

All the numbers in a line plus the number in the circle multiplied together equal 24. What is the number in the circle and fill in the other numbers.

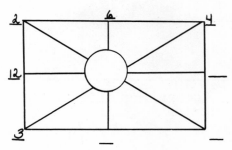

Answers

Circle is 2

From left to right: 2, 6, and 1.

Multiplying Four Numbers

$$35 \times 10 \times 9 \times 8 = ?$$

Multiply:

1. $35 \times 10 = 350$
2. $9 \times 8 = 72$
3. $35 \times 9 = 315$
4. $10 \times 8 = \underline{80}$
                       $25,200$

Check:

1. 350×72
2. $315 \times \underline{80}$

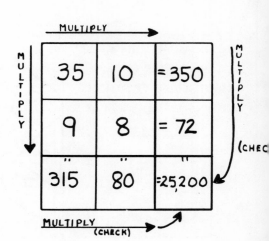

Magic Equilateral Triangles

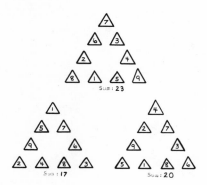

Calendar Base Five

Could you do one for Christmas, year 1969?

| | | | November 30331_5 | | 30331_5 | |
Sun.	Mon.	Tues.	Wed.	Thurs.	Fri.	Sat.
		1	2	3	4	10
11	12	13	14	20	21	22
23	24	30	31	32	33	34
40	41	42	43	(44)	100	101
102	103	104	110			

Mysterious Triangle

Can you move three dots and make a triangle in the opposite direction?

Answer

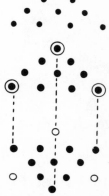

Move One Card

Procedure: Move one card from one group to another so that the sum of the figures in each group will then be equal.

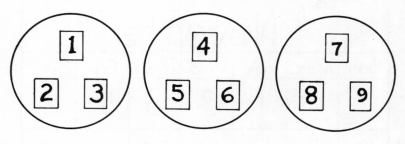

Solution

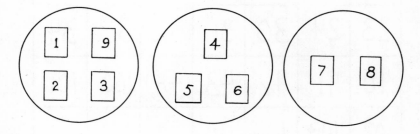

Stacking the Blocks

Procedure: The nine blocks are to be stacked in three equal piles, with the total value of the numbers on the blocks in each pile equal.

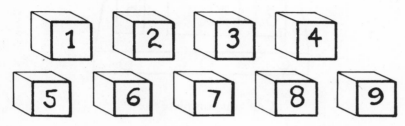

Solution

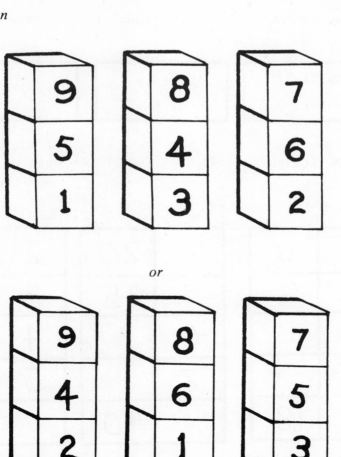

or

The Function Game

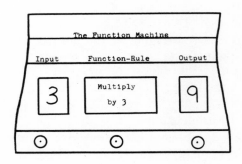

Can you complete these?

Function Rule	Function Rule	Function Rule
Multiply by 3	Multiply by 5	

Input	Output	Input	Output	Input	Output
2	6	4	20	2	4
3	9		25	3	6
4		6		4	8
5		7		5	
	18		40		12

How Well Do You Listen?

This problem should be read aloud to test class retentiveness:

A jetliner leaves New York with 50 people on it. It flies to Chicago and 20 passengers get off while seven others get on. The plane continues to Denver where 15 people get off and nine others get on. It then flies to San Francisco and lets off 12 passengers while 28 get on. It then flies to Santa Fe where no one gets off but it picks up five more passengers. It then flies to Dallas and leaves off two and picks up ten. The plane goes on to New Orleans with 22 people getting off and seven getting on. From New Orleans the jet lands in Miami where it unloads completely. The question: How many stops did the plane make?

Answer: seven (Chicago   Dallas
                   Denver   New Orleans
                   San Francisco   Miami)
                   Santa Fe

Crazy Clock

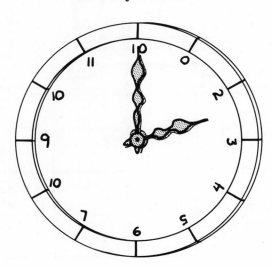

See if you find all the crazy mistakes that were made in this clock.

Answer

1. The hour hand is in the wrong position for 2 or 3 o'clock.
2. The 10 by the minute hand should be 12.
3. The 0 should be 1.
4. The 5 is upside down.
5. The number following 7 should be 8, not 10.

Fraction Maze

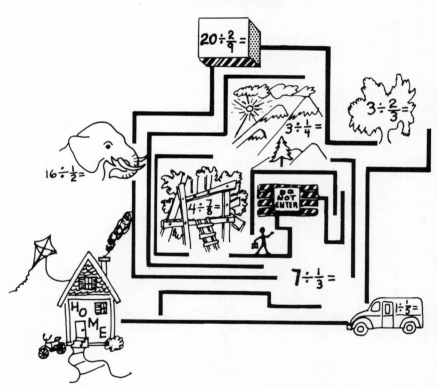

The children have to get the boy out of the maze and back home. In order to pass through the obstacles, they must have the correct answer to the problem. The first one to find the correct path and answer each problem correctly is the winner.

Mix and Match

Directions: Draw a solid line to the problems that are correct.
Draw a dotted line to the problems that are incorrect.

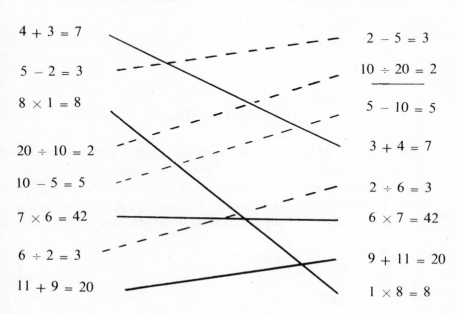

$4 + 3 = 7$	$2 - 5 = 3$
$5 - 2 = 3$	$10 \div 20 = 2$
$8 \times 1 = 8$	$5 - 10 = 5$
$20 \div 10 = 2$	$3 + 4 = 7$
$10 - 5 = 5$	$2 \div 6 = 3$
$7 \times 6 = 42$	$6 \times 7 = 42$
$6 \div 2 = 3$	$9 + 11 = 20$
$11 + 9 = 20$	$1 \times 8 = 8$

Dino the Brontosaurus

One of the largest and best known dinosaurs, he was called "Thunder Lizard" because the ground supposedly shook when he walked. Count the numbers to find out how many feet in length he was and then divide by 4 to find out how many tons he weighed.

Solution
80 feet in length
20 tons in weight

Geometric Math

The purpose of this exercise is to acquaint the children with substituting numerals for letters and help them gain a greater understanding of relation symbols. Examples of this exercise are below. Numerals may be replaced by letters simply by asking the child what letters would we use to create this problem? $5 \times 2 = 5 \times 3$

	yes	no

$a \times c = a \times b$
$5 \times 2 = 5 \times 3$

$d \times c + b > a \times a + d$
$3 \times 5 + 7 > 4 \times 4 + 3$

$c - a \times b \not< d - b \times a$
$10 - 1 \times 4 \not< 9 - 4 \times 1$

$a \times b + c \geqq b \times c + a$
$4 \times 8 + 5 \geqq 8 \times 5 + 4$

$b + e \times c - a \not\equiv f - b + d \times c$
$2 + 5 \times 3 - 1 \not\equiv 6 - 2 + 4 \times 3$

How Old Is He?

Add up the numbers you find in the funny man and find his age.

Answer: 59

Making Numerals

First graders frequently have great difficulty in learning to form numerals correctly. Learning devices are not only helpful but add fun and creativity as well. Below are suggestions to help children in forming nine basic numerals. After discussing these methods ask the children, "What can you make using these picture numerals?"

Method	*Numeral*	
A telephone pole without any wires.	1	
Draw a scooter and a stick figure.	2	
Draw part of a flower.	3	
Draw two prongs of a rake.	4	

Draw half an apple with the stem and a straight line.	5	5 5
Draw the tail of a snake.	6	6
Draw half a box.	7	7
We're going on a picnic and will travel on a curvy road (which is the letter s). We had to stop and go straight home because we forgot the lunch.	8	S 8
Draw a stick man with a pack on his back.	9	9

Magic Answer Exercise

The following exercise is good fun and good learning too. Look at the directions:

	Example
	10
1. Pick a number	
2. Double the number you choose	$10 \times 2 = 20$
3. Add the number I tell you to add to it	Add $4 = 24$
4. Divide by 2	$24 \div 2 = 12$
5. Subtract your original number from step 4	$12 - 10 = 2$
6. I can tell your final number	2

Explanation: The answer is always one half of the number I tell you to add: ½ of 4 is 2.

Figure out the examples and help Helen ski her way to a cup of hot chocolate.

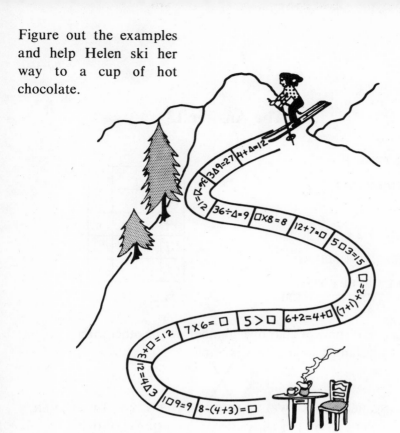

The following equations appear along the ski path:

$3\triangle 9=27$ $4+\triangle=12$

$?=?-?$

$36\div\triangle=9$ $\square\times 8=8$ $12+7=\square$ $5\square 3=15$

$(7+1)+2=\square$

$3+\square=12$ $7\times 6=\square$ $5>\square$ $6+2=4+\square$

$12=4\triangle 3$

$1\square 9=9$ $8-(4+3)=\square$

The Answer 1

THINK OF A NUMBER			
5			
ADD 3 — 8			
MULTIPLY BY 2 — 16			
SUBTRACT 4 — 12			
DIVIDE BY 2 — 6			
SUBTRACT NUMBER — 1			

THINK OF
A NUMBER

ADD 3

MULTIPLY
BY 2

SUBTRACT 4

DIVIDE BY 2

SUBTRACT
NUMBER

ANSWER EVERY TIME   1

Put some numbers of your own in the other three columns and try it again!

The Answer 13

THINK OF A NUMBER

MULTIPLY BY 2

ADD 26

DIVIDE BY 2

SUBTRACT NUMBER

ANSWER EVERY TIME 13

4			
8			
34			
17			
13			

Put some of your own numbers in the other three columns and try this example.

RUNNING BEAR HAS TWELVE HORSES, TWENTY-FOUR BEAVER
PELTS, TWELVE FOX PELTS, AND THIRTY BUFFALO HIDES.
AT THE TRADING POST HE CAN GET THE FOLLOWING PRICES:

HORSES............. TEN DOLLARS PER HORSE

BEAVER............ TWENTY-FIVE DOLLARS PER PELT

FOX................ TEN DOLLARS PER PELT

BUFFALO........... TWENTY DOLLARS PER HIDE

WHICH WOULD BRING THE HIGHEST PRICE?
WHICH WOULD BRING THE LOWEST PRICE?
IF HE SOLD EVERYTHING HOW MUCH WOULD HE GET?

Answer: *buffalo*
horses and fox
$1,440

Spelling Bee

Count the letters of each word to figure the sum of both. When the child knows the answer number, he must therefore look for a spelling word with the correct numbers. Have the pupils make their own list and choose new words.

1. d o g + _____ = 10
   1 – 2 – 3   1 – 2 – 3 – 4 – 5 – 6 – 7

2. h o u s e + _____ = 9
   1 – 2 – 3 – 4 – 5   1 – 2 – 3 – 4

Word List

playmate	catchers
company	mother
house	bird
toe	sum

Answers: 1. company
                     2. bird

Nine Tables

Lay a pencil over the number by which you wish to multiply nine. The *number* of digits visible on the *left* will be the number of *tens*. The *number* of digits visible on the *right* will be the number of *ones*. For example: Cover the number 7.

    There are 6 digits, or 6 tens on the left   = 60
    There are 3 digits, or 3 ones on the right   = 3
                  So; 7×9 . . . . = $\overline{63}$

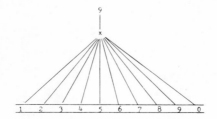

Roman Numeral Cryptogram

Since sixth graders enjoy working with mechanical objects this game centers around a typewriter. The keys and Roman numerals represent the letters in the following way: Q is I, W is II, E is III, R is IV, T is V, Y is VI, U is VII, I is VIII, O is IX, P is X, and so on through XXVI. The teacher will put the following numerals on the board as an example: XVI, III, XIX, XIX, IX! This is one word. By substituting the appropriate letters the students get HELLO! By leaving a double space it's a new word.

QWERTYUIOP
ASDFGHJKL
ZXCVBNM

Fun with Roman Numerals

Fred said, "Billy, I bet I can show you that half of nine is four."
"I bet you can't," said Billy. "Half of eight is four."
"Watch me," said Fred. "First, I write nine as a Roman numeral. Next, I draw a line through the middle like this. Then I erase the lower half. The half that remains is four. So half of nine is four. Isn't that right?"
"Yes, you win," agreed Billy.

Step 1   *Step 2*   *Step 3*

IX   ⫢X   IV

1. Can you show that half of 11 is six?

2. Can you show that half of 12 is seven?

3. Can you take away one from nine and leave ten?

4. Can you add one to two and make it six?

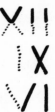

Magic Arrow

Move and replace three circles so that the arrow is pointing *up* instead of *down*.

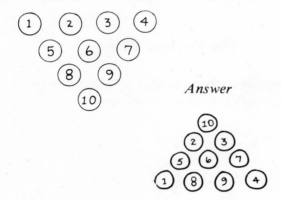

Answer

Puzzle

Ask the boys and girls to answer all of the problems. Then have them use a light color to make a mosaic. They will let you grade it and then they may darken their colors if they wish. A code can be set up or the children can choose any colors they want.

1-red	7-brown	14-orange	25-dark green
2-blue	8-black	15-yellow	27-red
3-orange	9-purple	16-light green	
4-green	10-light green	20-grey	
5-yellow	11-light blue	22-violet	
6-pink	12-red	24-navy blue	

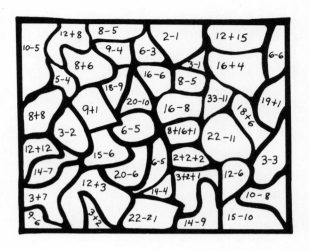

The Perfect Cross

Move only one coin so that you have a perfect cross of four down and three across—with still seven coins there.

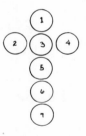

Answer: Place the bottom coin on coin number three.

The Magic Watch

Show a person the face (dial) of a watch, and ask him to think of a certain hour. But warn him not to tell you the hour he has in mind. You will tell him that, for you are going to "read his mind."

Then tap on the face of the dial with a pencil. Have the person count the taps to himself. He will start with the number of the hour he selected, and add 1 at the first tap, and so on. Have the person stop you when he has reached 20. On that tap—the twentieth tap—your pencil will be on the hour the person had in mind.

Key

Point here and there to any numbers about the face of the watch as you tap. But when you tap the *eighth* time, the pencil must be on 12. Then go around the numbers on the watch in backward order, as 11, 10, 9, 8, and so on until the person calls out to stop. The pencil will point to the hour he had in mind.

Number Puzzle

$1\frac{1}{2}\times\frac{1}{2}=$

$^{10}\!/_4=?/10$

$2\times3=$

$(2\times3)+2=$

$2\frac{1}{2}+2\frac{1}{2}=$

$2+4+5+1=$

$7+7=$

$^{10}\!/_7=?/10$

$^{12}\!/_2=?$

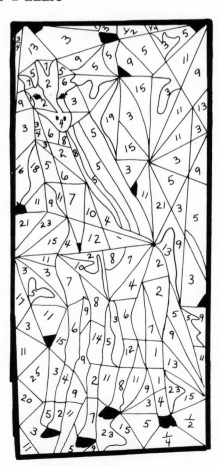

Answer the above questions. Color in the numbers of the puzzle that correspond to your answers.

What kind of animal is this?

Where would you find him?

Treasure Hunt

1″ = 2 miles

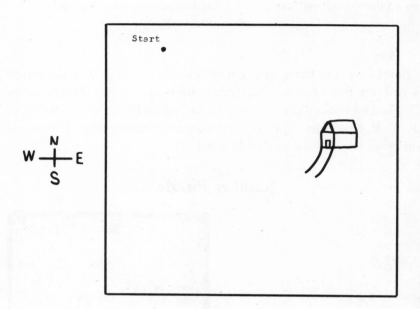

A Treasure Hunt

Four miles east of the start
Is your first resting place.
Then go south for two miles
And keep a steady pace.

Turn west and travel three miles—
It is a long way.
Then head south one mile
And have a stay.

Go slowly towards the door of the house
For five miles you will aim.
And when you find the treasure,
It is the end of the game.

Which Way to a Hundred

Draw a line through 20 numbers so that when added together they equal 100.

6	3	7	6	5	4
8	2	9	4	2	9
5	7	8	5	6	8
4	6	5	7	3	5
8	9	4	2	8	4

100

Answer

Tails Up

Using three coins, place them in the order shown below.

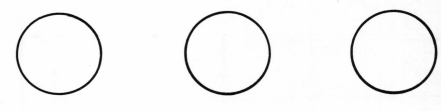

Heads   Tails   Heads

The problem is to make exactly three moves, turn over two coins each time you make a move, and end up with all three coins being tails up.

Answer

The coins will be lettered A, B, and C for identification. On the first move, turn coins B and C over. On the second move, turn coins A and C. On the last move, turn coins B and C. All three coins will be tails up.

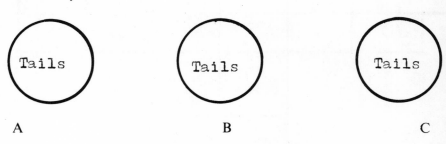

A   B   C

Guess Rules and Complete Squares

Guess the rules of the completed squares on top of each section of squares. After finding the rules of how each of these numbers were obtained, finish the empty squares below them using these rules.

2	14	12
5	35	33
3		
7		
1		
9		
10		
4		

10	15	11
1	6	2
4		
9		
12		
5		
7		
15		

Answer: multiply by 7
then subtract 2

Answer: add 5
then subtract 4